DENOU

by John Morton

ISBN 978-0-573-13357-2

concordtheatricals.co.uk
concordtheatricals.com

FOR AMATEUR PRODUCTION ENQUIRIES

UNITED KINGDOM AND WORLD
EXCLUDING NORTH AMERICA
licensing@concordtheatricals.co.uk

020-7054-7298

Each title is subject to availability from Concord Theatricals, depending upon country of performance.

---

written permission of the publisher. No one shall share this title, or part of this title, to any social media or file hosting websites.

The moral right of John Morton to be identified as author of this work has been asserted in accordance with Section 77 of the Copyright, Designs and Patents Act 1988.

USE OF COPYRIGHTED MUSIC

A licence issued by Concord Theatricals to perform this play does not include permission to use the incidental music specified in this publication. In the United Kingdom: Where the place of performance is already licensed by the PERFORMING RIGHT SOCIETY (PRS) a return of the music used must be made to them. If the place of performance is not so licensed then application should be made to PRS for Music (www.prsformusic.com). A separate and additional licence from PHONOGRAPHIC PERFORMANCE LTD (www.ppluk.com) may be needed whenever commercial recordings are used. Outside the United Kingdom: Please contact the appropriate music licensing authority in your territory for the rights to any incidental music.

USE OF COPYRIGHTED THIRD-PARTY MATERIALS

Licensees are solely responsible for obtaining formal written permission from copyright owners to use copyrighted third-party materials (e.g., artworks, logos) in the performance of this play and are strongly cautioned to do so. If no such permission is obtained by the licensee, then the licensee must use only original materials that the licensee owns and controls. Licensees are solely responsible and liable for clearances of all third-party copyrighted materials, and shall indemnify the copyright owners of the play(s) and their licensing agent, Concord Theatricals Ltd., against any costs, expenses, losses and liabilities arising from the use of such copyrighted third-party materials by licensees.

IMPORTANT BILLING AND CREDIT REQUIREMENTS

If you have obtained performance rights to this title, please refer to your licensing agreement for important billing and credit requirements.

DENOUEMENT is an original Lyric Theatre Belfast commission. Premiere date was 7th September 2020. This was a Listen At The Lyric premiere. The writer is John Morton. Directed by Gareth Nicholls, Artistic Director at the Traverse Theatre, Producers Linda Crooks, Traverse Theatre Jimmy Fay, Lyric Theatre, Sound Designer Michael John McCarthy, Dramaturg Rebecca Mairs, Sound Engineer Ian Vennard. The cast was as follows:

EDEL...Marie Jones

LIAM... Ian McElhinney

MAIREAD ....Nicky Harley

KEITH.. Patrick McBrearty

NIAMH.. Leah McGregor

LYRIC

The Lyric Theatre in Belfast is a playhouse for everyone to enjoy. It's a creative hub for theatre-making, a safe space for nurturing talent and has an unwavering passion for creating meaningful connections through theatre arts.

We've always done things a little differently at the Lyric. Right from its modest beginnings in 1968, this special place has been a springboard for internationally acclaimed playwrights, poets and actors. As Northern Ireland's only full-time theatre to produce its own productions from page to stage, we care deeply about maintaining a high-quality, diverse and inclusive programme that captures the imaginations of our audiences leaving them changed, charged and empowered.

Great writing is in our bones. Building on the canon of work from previously premiered playwrights like Brian Friel, Christina Reid, Marie Jones and many more, the Lyric continues to nurture creative talent and amplify new voices.

PRINCIPAL FUNDERS

TRAVERSE THEATRE

The Traverse is a champion of performance, experience and discovery. Enabling people to access and engage with theatre is our fundamental mission, and we want our work to represent, speak to and be seen by the broadest cross section of society. We are specialists in revealing untold perspectives in innovative ways. This is our role as Scotland's new writing theatre and a commitment that drives each strand of our work.

Our year-round programme bursts with new stories, live and digital performances that challenge, inform and entertain our audiences. We empower artists and audiences to make sense of the world today, providing a safe space to question, learn, empathise and – crucially – encounter different people and experiences. Conversation and the coming together of groups are central to a democratic society, and we champion equal expression and understanding for the future of a healthy national and international community.

The Traverse would not exist without our over-arching passion for developing new stories and embracing the unexplored. We work with bold voices and raw talent – with an emphasis on the Scottish-based – to create the art, artists, and performances that can be seen on our platforms year-round. We invest in ideas and support individuals to push boundaries by placing them at the centre of their own practice, and through projects like Class Act, Traverse Young Writers, and First Stages the continual relationship between artist development and performance can be seen in powerful action.

We aim for the timely stories and creative programmes that start life with us to have a global impact, through tours, co-productions, digital life, and translations. We are critically acclaimed and recognised the world over for our originality and artistic risk, which we hope will create some of the most talked-about plays, productions, directors, writers, and actors for years to come.

The Traverse's commitment to bringing new and bold storytelling to global audiences is amplified in Edinburgh each August, when international audiences make the Traverse programme – often referred to as the 'beating heart of the Fringe' – their first port of call in a city overflowing with entertainment offerings.

Our past successes drive our present and future direction, in the knowledge that our unique ability to nurture new talent and engage audiences through ambitious storytelling has never been more crucial in creating and sustaining a vibrant theatre landscape that reflects and challenges the world today.

The Traverse is supported by Creative Scotland and the City of Edinburgh Council. The Traverse has received additional support from the Scottish Government's Performing Arts Venues Relief Fund.

Traverse Theatre (Scotland) is a Limited Company (Registered Number SC076037) and a Scottish Charity (Registered Number SC002368) with its Registered Office at 10 Cambridge Street, Edinburgh, Scotland, EH1 2ED.

Find out more about our work: traverse.co.uk

CHARACTERS

EDEL – 60's, keeping it together, preparing for the worst, trying to say goodbye

LIAM – 60's, unshaven, addled, scrambling to finish his memoirs

Voices:

MAIREAD – 30's, their daughter, a voice.

KEITH – 30's, their son in law, a voice.

NIAMH – 10, their granddaughter, a voice.

VARIOUS – Lost voices heard through transmission

SETTING

The action takes place in the kitchen of a small farmhouse during the end of times. Ireland.

TIME

2048

AUTHOR'S NOTES

-noun

1. the final resolution of the intricacies of a plot, as of a drama or novel.
2. the place in the plot at which this occurs.
3. the outcome or resolution of a doubtful series of occurrences.

ACKNOWLEDGMENTS

Jimmy Fay and everyone at the Lyric Theatre for all of their tireless and ongoing support.

The brilliant actors who have helped shape this play and breathed life into these characters during its development. Des Manahan and Geraldine Plunkett. Anna Healy and Frankie McCafferty. Bríd Brennan and Karl Johnson. Stuart McQuarrie and Lucianne McEvoy. Ian McElhinney and Marie Jones.

Gareth Nicholls and everyone at Traverse Theatre for all their help and support.

Thanks to Jeffrey Gormley, Ger Cody, Frances Arnold, Andrew O'Leary, Ken McGuire, Niamh Moroney and Kevin Mooney for their help and support over the years that this play has been developing.

And to Rebecca Mairs, for believing in this play in the first place. I cannot thank you enough.

For my grandparents, Jim, Vera, John and Mollie.
And my parents, Vincent and Breda.

(The kitchen of a small farmhouse. It is a well decorated blend of old and new, having been gradually renovated over the years. Modern fittings compliment the original ones. Above the sink and kitchen top is a window with a view of the mountain that rises up above just beyond the land. A basket full of dirty clothes lies by a washing machine. Everything has an air of upheaval about it. There's a lot of dust around, maybe neglect but it could be from something else.)

(To the left of stage there is the back door leading to a farmyard. Next to the door lies an assortment of footwear under a radiator. Next to this is an umbrella stand with no umbrellas and an upright shotgun. Beside it is a shelf with books, a variety of assorted chargers and untidied bits and bobs lying strewn around. Downstage left is a desk with an old-fashioned typewriter sat on it. Empty, used glasses, discarded papers and books are also piled on the desk along with a stack of papers. To the right is the door into the unseen hallway. In the middle of the floor is the kitchen table with two chairs side by side in the middle. Empty drink bottles, small bags of drugs and used plates lie around the table. There is a laptop with an old orthopaedic armchair sat in front of it. Music can be heard loudly from a small,

portable speaker*. It's drowning out whatever noise may be outside.)

(Two figures are sat here. It is very early in the morning and they've been up all night.)

*(***LIAM*** *sits at the typewriter. He is clacking away busily.)*

*(***EDEL*** *sits at the laptop. She is typing away at a measured but consistent pace. She goes back and forth between the laptop and a mobile phone she checks.)*

(They are disturbed by the sound of a huge crash from outside. It breaks them both from their work. ***EDEL*** *hits pause on the music. It stops dead. We hear what sounds like intermittent explosions in the far-off distance. This is the noise they were drowning out.)*

*(***LIAM*** *gets up and goes to the back door. He slowly and tentatively begins to open it.* ***EDEL*** *slowly gets to her feet as he does so. She gestures for him to slow down but he's not watching. With the door slightly ajar, he peeks out to see what happened outside. Satisfied, he opens it fully. Then he goes over, grabs his raincoat, and hastily throws it on. He picks up the shotgun and heads outdoors.* ***EDEL*** *gets up and goes over to the window. She watches for a few moments. She checks the backdoor to see where* ***LIAM*** *is. Then she goes over to the cabinet and opens it. She begins*

---

* A licence to produce DENOUEMENT does not include a performance licence for any third-party or copyrighted music. Licensees should create an original composition or use music in the public domain. For further information, please see Music Use Note on page iii.

rooting around, looking for something. She finds an old holy medal on a knotted piece of string. She begins to unknot it before putting it around her neck and hiding it under her cardigan. She clasps her hands together and begins to say a prayer. She seems very unsure of herself. Her voice is low, muttering.)

EDEL. *(Muttering.)* Hail Mary... full of grace... the lord is with thee... blessed are... and blessed... is the fruit... *(Stops. Thinks.)* ...is the fruit of thy womb... Jesus...

(She stops. She can't remember anymore of it. She stares up at the ceiling for a few moments as if waiting for something to happen. But it doesn't. She goes over to the kitchen table and picks up a small bag of white powder. She pours some out onto a chopping board. She takes a knife and shapes it into a line. Then she sniffs it up in one go. **LIAM** *comes back in, coughing hard. He's holding onto some brown paper parcels. She stares at him expectantly, but he doesn't say anything. Explosions can still be heard in the distance.)*

...what was it?

LIAM. Van crashed straight into the ditch outside... total write off...

EDEL. I had the fear there that the reactor was gone.

LIAM. No, no... we're still good.

*(***LIAM*** leans into the door to close it shut. As he does this, he accidentally drops the shotgun.)*

(The clatter causes them both to jump.)

Ya fucker!

EDEL. Will you watch it with that thing?

LIAM. Sorry... sorry...

> (**EDEL** *walks over and picks up the gun. She checks it's okay and puts it back in its place.*)

> (**LIAM** *moves into the room, weighing up the various parcels.*)

EDEL. Did he crash it or did it crash itself?

LIAM. I don't know, it could have gone haywire... another car sped past me on the road, no one in the thing.

EDEL. Was he alright?

LIAM. It's bad enough out there already without having to worry about cars driving themselves around at full speed.

EDEL. The driver... is he alright?

LIAM. He went through the windscreen. Half of him anyway, his head was twisted around... blood streaming down the bonnet, so no, he's not alright. Not alright by any means.

EDEL. Yeah, but is he dead... or dying... what is it?

LIAM. Oh yeah, dead. Dead as you like. I doubt he felt anything. There were syringes all over the dash of the van... all his gear strewn about. It was just... carnage... the absolute state of him... driving around off his head like that...

EDEL. He could have killed someone.

LIAM. He'd be doing well. Not many options left if you wanted to give someone a belt of a car.

EDEL. Yeah... is it still a shit show outside?

LIAM. The shit show to end all shit shows.

EDEL. Did you see anyone?

LIAM. Not a sinner.

(**LIAM** *goes over to the table and throws down the parcels.*)

I took what he had left...

EDEL. You vulture.

LIAM. And his wallet...

(**LIAM** *throws the wallet down on the table. Then he produces a mobile phone and puts it down.* **EDEL** *immediately picks it up and checks it.*)

EDEL. And his phone...

LIAM. It's as dead as himself.

EDEL. Picking the bones clean.

LIAM. He won't have any use for it now, will he?

(**LIAM** *takes off his raincoat and hangs it up.* **EDEL** *starts rooting through the collection of chargers to see if anything fits.*)

EDEL. Might get some juice out of this.

LIAM. No point in the dead hoarding stuff.

EDEL. True that.

LIAM. Who knows how long more the arse will be dragged out of this?

EDEL. If that's the case we'll need to get more supplies.

LIAM. I'd say he was making a killing off people.

EDEL. Who?

LIAM. The dealer. The dead lad out on the road.

(*They both eagerly rifle through the bags of drugs at their disposal.*)

EDEL. There's enough cocaine here to kill a small horse.

LIAM. And enough ketamine to knock out several large horses.

EDEL. We're just being greedy now.

LIAM. Well, we can space it out if we need to.

(**EDEL** *examines a parcel that's been tagged.*)

EDEL. He must have been getting this stuff from the guards...

LIAM. Buying it?

EDEL. Taking it. There was a post in the community group a few weeks ago saying seized contraband was being looted from empty garda stations.

LIAM. Oh yeah.

EDEL. Lads just going in and helping themselves, not a bother on them.

LIAM. Well, I doubt the guards cared much.

EDEL. Probably took enough for themselves.

LIAM. Was I tell you about the guard at checkpoint a few weeks back?

EDEL. You were, yeah. With the coke falling out of his nostrils?

LIAM. That's it. And talking faster than you'd be used to from a guard.

EDEL. I wonder when they gave up.

LIAM. I'd say they had the sense to get out as soon as they could. "Fuck this racket, let's go and get off our chops."

EDEL. Well, better the drugs get used up than just sitting there in some abandoned station.

LIAM. Kills a bit of time when we're waiting around anyway...

EDEL. Is there any heroin?

LIAM. Why, would you do heroin?

EDEL. Yeah, I'd do it now probably. If we had some.

LIAM. We don't unfortunately. I'd say it's in high demand.

EDEL. Not a bad auld way to go.

LIAM. Better that than being cleaned out of it by a fuckin' robot car.

> (**EDEL** *checks her phone for a few moments. Then she goes over and checks on the laptop.*)
>
> (**LIAM** *begins cutting up lines of cocaine on the table.*)

Do you want one?

EDEL. I've just had one.

LIAM. Another then?

EDEL. I don't want Mairead seeing me with coke jitters.

LIAM. I'd say now she has bigger things to be worrying about than you coked off your tits.

EDEL. It's just not a good look.

LIAM. I'd say she'd get a kick out of it.

EDEL. It's been a very long time since she's seen me not sober...

LIAM. Any sign of her online?

EDEL. Not since last night...

LIAM. It'd be good to say goodbye to her again.

EDEL. And Patrick too.

> (**LIAM** *puts a key into a pile of cocaine and sniffs it up. It's strong and he gives a little shake.*)

(He wipes dust off his nose. Then he goes right back into cutting up the lines.)

LIAM. Remember the night I found the yokes in her coat pocket?

EDEL. All I remember is the screams of her when you dragged her into the house.

EDEL. Did we drop them soon after that? At a wedding?

LIAM. I think we did, in Clara.

EDEL. We hit the dancefloor hard that night.

LIAM. Oh yeah. We were the first ones on it. Did you ever think back on all the times you've been mad out of it thinking no one else could tell –

EDEL. – but they always can. I remember well my first time being on pills around my mother. I was never so delighted to see her.

(LIAM sniffs up two big lines of cocaine. He lets out a roar as it immediately hits him.)

LIAM. That's... the ticket!

(He turns back on the music on the laptop and starts to strut and dance around in an animated fashion. Watching him being so animated seems to spur EDEL on. She begins cutting up another line of cocaine and sniffs it right up.)*

The right head space... just fly through it... finish strong... we'll finish strong Edel... we will...

---

* A licence to produce DENOUEMENT does not include a performance licence for any third-party or copyrighted music. Licensees should create an original composition or use music in the public domain. For further information, please see Music Use Note on page iii

(They both move around the kitchen, dancing, stretching, warming themselves up. It's now become a morning ritual, getting ready for the day ahead or the lack thereof.)

(Then after a while they've had enough.)

EDEL. Last night has me spent...

LIAM. Broke up...

EDEL. I shouldn't have gone so hard.

LIAM. I know the feeling.

*(**EDEL** sits back down in her armchair.)*

EDEL. I wish I'd slept more...

LIAM. In general?

EDEL. No, I mean... the last few nights.

LIAM. No sleep now until the eternal sleep.

EDEL. Shouldn't have done that bump...

LIAM. Well, you definitely won't be sleeping now.

*(**LIAM** weighs up whether he's going to have another line or not. **EDEL** checks her laptop.)*

*(**LIAM** decides to go for it.)*

Ah, one more won't kill me.

*(**LIAM** takes a key of cocaine and sniffs it right up. **EDEL** seems rattled by something she's seen on her screen.)*

EDEL. Oh fuck...

LIAM. What is it?

EDEL. America, it's gone.

LIAM. What do you mean it's gone?

EDEL. Krissy messaged me. She said nothing's been heard from the States in a few hours.

LIAM. Well, maybe the internet is gone.

EDEL. No, she heard that the whole place is gone.

LIAM. Could be rumours.

EDEL. Rumours tend to be true these days.

LIAM. Like, how gone are we talking here?

EDEL. Wiped.

LIAM. Wiped?

EDEL. Wiped.

LIAM. It's coming here then?

EDEL. Yeah... shit...

> *(They compose themselves a moment. Then they seperate again and resume their busyness.)*

> *(LIAM rushes back to his desk and begins enthusiastically typing again. EDEL focuses in on her laptop. The sounds of destruction outside get momentarily louder.)*

LIAM. I have to get these finished... I have to...

> *(EDEL starts typing quickly on her laptop.)*

EDEL. I need to call the lads...

> *(She puts a call through on the laptop. We can hear a dial tone. But nothing seems to be coming. EDEL turns off the music entirely.)*

LIAM. Here, would you mind leaving the tunes on?

EDEL. Why?

LIAM. That racket outside is very distracting.

EDEL. I don't think the music is going to drown it out.

LIAM. The tunes are a good memory aid for writing.

EDEL. Yeah but I don't want to die listening to that shite.

LIAM. I wouldn't mind dying to this tune.

EDEL. Sorry, I'm not dying to some maudlin shite we haven't listened to in thirty years.

LIAM. You'd rather listen to the world coming in on us?

EDEL. If it was a belter tune maybe. Anyway, I don't think playing it loud is going to do anything for us when that shit comes.

> *(Not dwelling for too long,* **EDEL** *begins clicking the touchpad on her laptop impatiently. She hits it hard.)*

This bloody thing...

LIAM. Did the connection come back?

EDEL. Fits and starts.

LIAM. I'd say the cloud won't be long for the world.

EDEL. If the effort was put into shelter and relief that was put into the cloud we probably could have lasted longer.

LIAM. We have shelter and food...

EDEL. We, as in everyone.

> *(***EDEL*** goes back to the laptop, trying to get her connection to start up again. With nothing happening, she decides to check her phone.)*

LIAM. Do you still know short hand?

EDEL. *(Ignoring him.)* Come on Mairead...

LIAM. Didn't you learn shorthand at one stage?

EDEL. It says she's online anyway... she's –

LIAM. – Edel, didn't you learn shorthand before?

EDEL. *(Annoyed.)* What?

LIAM. Shorthand. Did you learn it?

EDEL. What are you on about?

LIAM. The little squiggles and things.

EDEL. Just a bit, I can't really remember it.

LIAM. You'd hardly be able to teach it to me?

EDEL. Now?

LIAM. Well... I don't know how it works.

EDEL. You're asking me now, right now, at this fucking minute, to teach you shorthand?

> *(He turns to her.)*

LIAM. No, I was wondering if there was a quick way of...

> *(She's just looking at him pithily. He gets defensive.)*

You don't know how long we have left!

EDEL. Yeah and I'm not wasting any of it on the construction of your memoirs Liam. I lived through most of them. Remember?

LIAM. Yes. I do.

EDEL. And that's enough for me. The memories in my head. Just tucked away there now as I get on with the rest of my business.

LIAM. Good for you but can we not waste our remaining time on sarcasm?

EDEL. Sarcasm?

LIAM. How long would shorthand take?

EDEL. You won't be learning it in the next five minutes, I'll tell you that for nothing.

LIAM. Alright. Thank you Edel.

EDEL. Is that sarcasm?

LIAM. No. It is not.

EDEL. Maybe try a few bullet points.

LIAM. No... no... it needs to be a finished work, y'know?

EDEL. A finished work... fuck my life. Well, I'll cross my fingers that you make your deadline so.

> (**LIAM** *wipes sweat from his brow and then resumes typing at a quick measured pace.*)

LIAM. Stream of consciousness so.

> (**EDEL** *tries to make her call again. But once more it doesn't go through. She checks her phone. After a few moments, there's an explosion outside, louder than before. They both stop what they're doing and listen. They wait for a follow up explosion, anticipating something closer.* **EDEL** *gets up to her feet.* **LIAM** *motions for her to stay still. They look at each other, helplessly. There's the loud sound of machinery in the distance, briefly. They hold themselves still, braced. Then the noise dies down. An eerie silence permeates again.*)

EDEL. It could be any second Liam.

LIAM. Yeah, yeah... I know.

> (*She's waiting for him to do something. He just stares at her, aimless, waiting for another sound. When it doesn't materialise he turns back to his task at hand.*)

EDEL. You really need to get this finished now?

LIAM. I'll rattle through it. Just a few more minutes.

> (**EDEL** *goes over to the window. She's peering out, trying to make out what lies in view.*)

EDEL. More smoke... same amount of fire.

LIAM. *(Murmuring, as he writes.)* "The chips were wrapped in newspaper I remember. It was something to read. Something to fill up the long silences." That doesn't sound...

> (*As he trails off,* **EDEL** *turns to him.*)

EDEL. Are you writing about that time we had the fight in Tramore?

LIAM. Hmmm? No...

EDEL. You just read it out there. I heard you.

LIAM. I didn't think you'd get that...

EDEL. Are you shit talking me in your stupid fucking memoirs?

LIAM. Don't be calling my memoirs stupid!

EDEL. What are you saying about me? Say it to my face.

LIAM. I'm not saying anything, I'm writing –

EDEL. – say it to my face.

LIAM. It's a literary recollection of a particular incident that's imbued with –

EDEL. – I'll imbue your hole with my foot in a minute. Say it to my face.

LIAM. It's not all about you though, is it? Give over now, I'm trying to write.

EDEL. Why do you've to be writing about that though?

LIAM. It's broad strokes, like.

EDEL. Can you not write your broad strokes about something nice, no? Instead of me throwing your burger into the sea?

(**LIAM** *has a small laugh to himself.*)

LIAM. Oh yeah, I forgot about the burger.

EDEL. Well, took a few years didn't it? Cos you surely moaned about it for a good long time.

LIAM. You were snapping. So funny now when you think of it.

EDEL. The funniest part was there part where I grabbed your burger out of your hand and fucked it into the sea.

LIAM. Well, it's funnier now.

EDEL. Don't be remembering me like that.

LIAM. Edel, it's just background to another story...

EDEL. What other story?

LIAM. Why do you want to know now?

EDEL. It's not like I'm going to have the time to read the fucking thing is it?

LIAM. Well, you never know...

EDEL. I do know.

LIAM. Ah, you don't. How many times have we thought we were done for since this started? And yet, here we are.

EDEL. Look, why is that bit of background necessary? Me being angry.

LIAM. It's not about you as such. I'm just writing about the way I was, like... you know.

EDEL. Do I?

LIAM. You do.

EDEL. I'm going to ring around and see how people are.

LIAM. Nothing from Mairead?

EDEL. Not yet. I'll check in with Maria and see if she's heard anything.

> (**EDEL** *rings a number on her phone. She does so while keeping an eye on the laptop screen.*)

(Into phone.) Hello? *(Pause.)* Maria! I heard America is wiped out. *(Pause.)* Did you hear that? *(Pause.)* Ah, not Canada. *(Pause.)* And poor Mexico too. *(Pause.)* It won't be long so. *(Pause.)* How's the head faring? *(Pause.)* Oh, I'm an absolute write off. *(Pause.)* I haven't danced like that in years. *(Pause.)* It was a great send off, wasn't it? *(Pause.)* How's Paddy? *(Pause.)* Oh no... the poor dog. *(Pause.)* Oh... *(Pause.)* We haven't seen ours in ages. *(Pause.)* No. *(Pause.)* Just trying to contact the kids in case this is the last of it. *(Pause.)* Right, right...

LIAM. *(Overlap.)* What year was it... thirty eight?

EDEL. *(Into phone.)* I get you... yeah...

LIAM. *(Overlap.)* The last hard winter... when was that Edel?

EDEL. *(To* **LIAM.***)* Whisht you now...

LIAM. *(To himself.)* Thirty nine? Was that the last one?

EDEL. *(Into phone.)* Liam is trying to finish his memoirs. Talking away to himself here.

LIAM. Talking to you...

EDEL. *(Into phone.)* How many died over there? *(Pause.)* They'll be missing the worst of it I suppose. *(Pause.)* Do you know what it was like? *(Pause.)* Okay. Just wondering how bad it was, you know? For the people who died. *(Pause.* **LIAM** *stops his typing a few seconds. He listens in.)* Yeah. *(Pause.)* Okay. I get you. *(Pause.)* That's something. *(Pause.)* Oh yeah, from the mountainside you can barely see the village anymore.

Just smoke and fire. *(Pause.)* Are you going to the top of the mountain for this other vigil? *(Pause.)* Well no, just another party but vigil sounds... more appropriate I suppose. Just call it a party, like. *(Pause.)* I don't know what time. *(Pause.)* No way? *(Pause.)* Imagine surviving this long and getting cleaned out of it by a falling drone? *(Pause.)* There are few worse ways. *(Laughs.)* True enough. *(Pause.)* The tablets? Ah, forget it Maria. *(Pause.)* Cyanide would be better. Or rat poison if you've any left? *(Pause.)* Ah, that's a pity. *(Pause.)* Yeah, we have the gun. You could have a loan of it but I don't know if it's worth travelling out now. *(Pause.)* Wouldn't be safe, no. *(Laughs.)* Alright, I'd better dash. Last of the loose ends here. *(Pause.)* Yeah... you too. Goodbye. I love you. Give Ryan my love too. *(Pause.)* I will... I will...

LIAM. Tell her I said goodbye too.

EDEL. *(Into phone.)* And Liam says he loves you too. *(Pause.)* It's been a pleasure knowing you, honestly. You've done a lot for me in the last few years and I've really valued your friendship. *(Laughs.)* I'll what? *(Laughs.)* Alright, off with you now and die screaming. *(Laughs.)* Okay, good luck, good luck. I love you too. *(Pause.)* Bye... bye... bye now... bye... bye... *(Hangs up.)* Ah... I'll miss her.

LIAM. Not for long.

EDEL. Yeah.

LIAM. What was she saying?

EDEL. She said I'll smell nicer when I'm burning alive.

LIAM. She's a gas woman.

EDEL. She is.

LIAM. And Ryan killed the dogs did he?

EDEL. Rat poison, yeah.

LIAM. Not the worst way to go in the broader spectrum of things…

EDEL. Ah, they're confused, the poor feckers. They're supposed to have an extra sense for this kind of thing –

LIAM. – yeah, an extra sense for disaster. I heard that.

EDEL. Barking for weeks before we even knew what was coming.

LIAM. And haven't stopped barking since. Non stop. I'm haunted by that sound now. Drilled into my soul. Your pets turning into harbingers of doom.

EDEL. I don't like them being out there alone…

LIAM. They're too mad to stay inside.

> (**EDEL** *sits back at the computer. Nothing there. She gets a message on her phone. She quickly begins replying. After a few moments, she clears her throat and rubs her nose.*)

EDEL. Chatting to Grá here. Her spelling is atrocious. I know we don't have much time left but come on, make it readable like.

LIAM. *(Whimsically.)* Panic will do that…

> (**EDEL** *stops what she's doing and turns to him.*)

EDEL. Are you quoting your memoirs there or are you saying something to me?

LIAM. I mean, if you're writing quick, like in a panic, it does nothing for the clarity.

> (**EDEL** *nods. She goes back to her phone.*)

EDEL. Leave a voice message, like…

LIAM. Too much.

EDEL. What do you mean?

LIAM. Voice messages... they can be very distressing for people.

EDEL. It's a distressing time... (**EDEL** *puts the phone down.*) I may leave her off here, she's making no sense at all.

LIAM. Can I ask you a question?

EDEL. Who else are you going to ask a question to?

LIAM. No one...

EDEL. Go on then.

LIAM. Wasn't it thirty we went to Amsterdam? Before that flood?

EDEL. Twenty six.

LIAM. I'm not sure it was twenty six.

> (**EDEL** *doesn't pay him much attention. She turns back to the laptop and begins typing.*)

I remember it well, thirty it was. The World Cup was going on.

EDEL. There was a World Cup going on in twenty six as well. It's every four years isn't it?

LIAM. It is, yeah. It was the one they had indoors.

EDEL. Liam, I know you went to get that done but I'd really prefer if you could just try and get in touch with Patrick.

LIAM. You haven't heard from him in weeks.

EDEL. Yeah and we're running out of time...

> (**EDEL**'s *mobile rings again.* **EDEL** *rushes to the end of a typed sentence. Then she hops up away from the computer and quickly answers.*)

(Into phone.) Hello? *(Pause.)* Ah Richie, you're still amongst us?

LIAM. Is that Richie? *(Pause.)* Throw him over to me here, will you?

> *(He goes to stand up. Then he stops all of a sudden.)*

No... actually... put him on speaker, will you?

> **(EDEL** *isn't paying him any attention.* **LIAM** *sits back down to resume his typing.)*

EDEL. *(Into phone.)* Yeah, this could be it. *(Pause.)* I'm not the better of last night. *(Pause.)* That's it... I haven't seen people jawing like that in a long time. Sandra's false teeth! *(Laughs. Pause.)* Ah no, I couldn't handle any more of Shane O'Gorman's depressing acoustic shite. As soon as he started into *Raglan Road* I was fit to shoot myself and the rest of ye along with me. *(Pause.)* Oh... *(Pause.)* I'm sorry. *(Pause.)* Where did she pass away? *(Pause.)* I never got to see Asia, in the end. *(Pause.)* It'll not be long so.

> **(LIAM** *stands up, harried and agitated.)*

LIAM. Just put him on speaker a second...

EDEL. *(Into phone.)* There's hardly anything stopping it at this point is there?

> **(EDEL** *is ignoring him so* **LIAM** *quickly walks around and stands in front of her.)*

LIAM. Look, just tell him I'm sorry for rolling over Shep a few years back. It was me who knocked him down and threw his body in the ditch. I didn't say anything when it happened, I don't know why, I think I was paralysed by the shame in a way. It was a dark time for me and killing an innocent dog just compounded it. *(Pause.)* Anyway, it's out now. So if you could just tell him I'm sorry, that'd be great.

EDEL. *(Into phone.)* Did you hear that? *(Pause.)* No. *(To* **LIAM.***)* Do you not just want to tell him that yourself?

LIAM. No time to be repeating myself Edel.

> (**LIAM** *goes straight back over to his desk and resumes writing.)*

EDEL. *(Into phone.)* Sorry to be holding you up there but the jist of it is that Liam is sorry for rolling over Shep a few years back. *(Pause.)* Yeah, it was him. Sorry. Who did you think it was? (**LIAM** *resumes typing, muttering to himself as he does.)* Paddy Grehan... well, yeah, sounds like something he'd do. Or have done. *(Pause.)* Well, we can't hold grievances now. Not anymore. *(Pause.)* You dirty fecker! I didn't know ye had a thing.

LIAM. What's he saying?

EDEL. He said he fingered your sister behind the graveyard wall when they were seventeen.

LIAM. Don't be telling me this now! For fuck sake...

> (**EDEL** *lets out a loud, dirty laugh into the phone.)*

EDEL. Well Richie, that was a nice surprise to drop at the end.

LIAM. And poor Karen dead nearly ten years now.

EDEL. Nearly twelve now. *(Into phone.)* Yeah, twelve years. We didn't feel it, did we?

LIAM. I hope he walked her home afterwards.

EDEL. *(Into phone.)* He said he hopes you walked her home after. *(Pause.)* He did...

LIAM. Good... well, tell him I said goodbye anyway and all the best.

EDEL. *(Into phone.)* He said he loves you. *(Pause.* **LIAM** *says nothing.)* He loves you too he says.

LIAM. *(Not paying much attention.)* Fuck this fucking shit anyway...

> *(He tries to fix a paper jam in the typewriter. It's not working like he wants.)*

Now's not the time to be acting up you stupid fuckin' bollocks of a thing!

EDEL. *(Into phone.)* I'll let you go Richie. *(Pause. Laughs.)* Go on. *(Pause.)* Ah, stop. *(Pause.)* Bit late in the game. *(Pause.)* Yeah, save it for Tara. *(Pause.)* Give her my best... *(Pause.)* Oh, sorry to hear it. I hope she wakes up before... *(Pause.)* Yeah well, can't say every goodbye. You've been a great friend Richie, I hope it passes easy for you. *(Pause.)* Yeah, you too. Goodbye. *(Pause.)* Rest well. *(Hangs up.)* He had to sedate Tara, she went a bit hysterical there.

LIAM. Wouldn't blame her.

> *(EDEL says nothing. She gets up and goes over to the window to take a look outside. LIAM begins absentmindedly humming the tune of the 19th century Irish air ["THE DAWNING OF THE DAY"] as he types.)*

EDEL. – fuck up.

> *(Brutally silenced, LIAM just composes himself and continues typing silently. Not seeing any change outside. EDEL returns to the table. Nothing is said for a few moments. EDEL keeps an eye on the laptop, intermittently flicking aimlessly through her phone. LIAM hits a snag with the typewriter. He keeps hammering a button, increasingly more agitated. The noise he's making is too much for her after a while.)*

Will you just use the laptop or the tablet or –

LIAM. – I'm not doing it Edel, we're back to basics here.

EDEL. It'll speed things up.

LIAM. Technology's been failing for weeks. I want a definitive document. Proof in my hand.

EDEL. That you existed?

LIAM. That I lived.

EDEL. Years of downloading and pirating and this is what you're reduced to.

LIAM. Yeah and where are we now? Internet is fucked, cloud is bollocksed, your photos reduced to digital rot. No, bollocks to that. I want hard copies.

EDEL. A lot of unnecessary clutter.

LIAM. Better than everything disappearing.

> (**LIAM** *gets it fixed. He stops and takes a deep breath and settles himself. He goes back to the typing feverishly.* **EDEL** *is pacing around, occasionally checking the laptop. Then she goes over to a shelf and starts busily rooting through it. She's making enough noise to visibly irritate* **LIAM.** *She stops what she's doing a second.)*

EDEL. Did you throw all the books out of here?

> (**LIAM** *is mouthing something to himself as he types, paying her no attention.)*

Here, you didn't throw out that Bible did you?

LIAM. The big one I took from the church?

EDEL. I just thought of it when I was talking to Maria. She was saying people were looking for them at the vigil.

LIAM. Party.

EDEL. Vigil... party... whatever. We did have one though... or am I making that up?

LIAM. It was taking up too much space. Threw it out years ago.

EDEL. You'd wonder how many of those relics people kept onto.

LIAM. It's just a novelty now.

EDEL. Not for the diehards...

LIAM. Ironic tat in pubs and cafés... sacred hearts and Virgin Mary statues...

EDEL. They weren't long becoming pubs and cafés...

LIAM. Museums...

EDEL. Museums...

LIAM. You'd forget it was even a thing anymore.

EDEL. Yeah... it's just... seeing Ella Kavanagh last night on the other side of the bonfire while everyone else was dancing... she stood there for about fifteen minutes... just murmuring to herself, her hands clasped. I couldn't make out what she was saying to herself, but it had to be prayers.

LIAM. Ah, she was very high in fairness.

EDEL. She was high enough I suppose.

LIAM. Off her tits.

EDEL. Yeah but... I don't know. I never felt that peaceful, even with the drugs... not since this kicked off.

LIAM. Well, from what I can remember there's a real lack of practical advice in the Bible so I wouldn't worry about it.

(**EDEL** *doesn't reply. She checks her phone again, scrolling through messages.*)

(As he types.) When did I start working on these? Is it three months?

EDEL. Whenever it was, I didn't give a bollocks then Liam and I don't give one now.

LIAM. Mind. That could be the last thing you say to me...

> (**EDEL** *taps her keyboard a bit more aggressively.* **LIAM** *tries to take his finished page out of the typewriter, but it's gotten stuck again. He tries to gently remove it.)*

EDEL. Patrick saw my last message.

LIAM. Did I leave my eyedrops in that drawer?

EDEL. He's online. Somewhere.

LIAM. Or will leave it?

EDEL. Or he was at least. That's good.

LIAM. I don't want to risk blinding meself for the rest of it though...

EDEL. If the two of us were trying to get through to Patrick we'd have more of a chance.

LIAM. There's any number of things he could be doing now instead of hanging around screens.

EDEL. Do you not want to talk to your son while you still can?

> *(The paper is yanked roughly from the typewriter.)*

LIAM. Fuckin' thing! It'll give me a heart attack before the end!

EDEL. Then stop typing!

LIAM. I want to get it finished!

EDEL. It's not the end of the...

(She stops herself short. She drags herself away from the laptop. She goes over towards the window. She picks up something from the sink.)

This steak is nearly defrosted.

LIAM. Alright...

*(**LIAM** puts a new sheet of paper into the typewriter. **EDEL** peers out the window, wiping some dust from the glass. **EDEL** stops as a thought strikes her.)*

EDEL. Is today our anniversary?

LIAM. It is, yeah.

*(**EDEL** nods. **LIAM** takes a deep breath. Composes himself. Applies himself to calmly putting the new sheet in. Going back to the pile of drugs, **EDEL** methodically chops out another line.)*

(Then she snorts it up. Energised, she picks up her phone.)

EDEL. I'll ring Kate. See how she's getting on down below.

(She picks up her mobile and dials a number. Not soon after, from outside, some dogs start howling and scraping at the kitchen door.)

LIAM. The boys are back.

EDEL. Ah no...

LIAM. What will I do?

EDEL. Let them in, just to give them a bit of comfort before it happens –

LIAM. – no way. They're too noisy, I'll get nothing done.

(Then, his mobile rings. **LIAM** *jumps a bit as he has the volume up too loud.)*

Who's this now? Fuck sake...

(He picks up the mobile. **EDEL** *waits for her call to pick up.* **LIAM** *tentatively answers his.)*

(They both have to talk louder to be heard over the howling dogs.)

(Into phone.) Hello? *(Pause.)* Ah, how's things Kev? *(Pause.)* Oh, stop. *(Pause.)* Up the walls man. Yourself? *(Pause.)* There's a rake of stuff up here if you're stuck. We could do a trade for some booze maybe cos we brought all ours up last week... *(Pause.)* Ah, it was anticlimactic in a way. *(Pause.)* Yeah, stay in. You wouldn't want to be going out in this if you can help it.

EDEL. *(Into phone.)* Hello! Kate? *(Pause.)* No, it's Edel.

LIAM. *(Into phone.)* Ah shit, that's terrible.

EDEL. *(Into phone.)* Edel I said... can you hear me?

LIAM. *(Into phone.)* Funny old world, eh?

EDEL. *(Into phone.)* Edel. *(Pause.)* Can you hear me?

LIAM. *(Into phone.)* I will, I will. Goodnight to you.

EDEL. *(Into phone.)* Lovely to chat all the same.

LIAM. *(Into phone.)* No, it's the dogs making a racket. Gone mad they are.

EDEL. *(Into phone.)* I see *(Pause.)* Oh...

LIAM. *(Into phone.)* I don't know man. *(Pause.)* They say animals have an extra sense for this craic, don't they?

EDEL. *(Into phone.)* Are you going up to the top for this vigil?

LIAM. *(Into phone.)* Yeah, it'd be like that I suppose. Or the trees.

EDEL. *(Into phone.)* It's dragging the arse out of it alright...

LIAM. *(Into phone.)* Lovely to hear it Kev.

EDEL. *(Into phone.)* Oh, the best view but...

LIAM. *(Into phone.)* I found that now, that particularly to be a very comforting aspect of the whole thing, you know?

EDEL. *(Into phone.)* I don't know if I want to watch it happen...

LIAM. *(Into phone.)* The trees probably have a better idea than we do.

EDEL. *(Into phone.)* But I'm not sure...

LIAM. *(Into phone.)* They could sense it coming before we did.

EDEL. *(Into phone.)* So funny that you're listening to that tune. *(Pause.)* In the background.

LIAM. *(Into phone.)* Lovely to hear it Kev.

EDEL. *(Into phone.)* Yeah, that was it. *(Pause.)* First dance at the wedding.

LIAM. *(Into phone.)* You'd be a fine man for a eulogy if there was time.

EDEL. *(Into phone.)* Yeah, this day twenty-nine years ago, would you believe?

LIAM. *(Into phone.)* Well, if I'm not talking to you again, rest well my man.

EDEL. *(Into phone.)* Yeah, when we didn't give two shits about anything.

LIAM. *(Into phone.)* That's it now.

EDEL. *(Into phone.)* Yeah, all ahead of us.

LIAM. *(Into phone.)* Good luck now old friend. Ride easy.

*(**LIAM** puts the phone down. Unsure of what to do with his hands, he decides to rub the tiredness from his eyes.)*

EDEL. *(Into phone.)* Take care of yourself pet. *(Pause.)* I will, I will. Rest well. Rest well. Bye... bye... bye... bye...

*(She hangs up. The sound of the dogs has gone by now. Both of them sit uncertainly for a few moments. **EDEL** weighs up both the cocaine and her tobacco and decides to start rolling a cigarette. A dull, churning noise outside. **LIAM** perks up, trying to listen. The sound of animals barking in the distance. The dogs are gone again. **LIAM** goes back to his typing.)*

*(**EDEL** finishes rolling her smoke before deciding to make another call.)*

The signal is getting worse here. If Patrick is trying to get through to us...

LIAM. Look, think the best of it Edel. He's probably enjoying himself. I'd say London is rife with chemsex parties and death raves and gang bangs and the whole lot.

EDEL. Yeah, well if that's the case I hope he takes a breather to ring his mother.

*(This inspires something in **LIAM**. He types quickly. He's not minding **EDEL**.)*

LIAM. He's been living a good life Liam.

*(**LIAM**'s typing pace slows down but then he picks it back up again.)*

LIAM. Good for him...

EDEL. Yeah. It is good for him.

(**LIAM** *doesn't reply.* **EDEL** *sticks a slow, precise middle finger up behind* **LIAM***'s back. She holds it, waiting for him to turn around. But he doesn't. She holds it a second longer.*)

(*But he's not noticing. Then she goes back to her phone and makes a call.*)

Come on...

(*The call rings out. Dejected, she slowly puts the phone down.*)

That was Kev you were talking to there, yeah?

LIAM. Yeah?

EDEL. What's new?

LIAM. He said Noel Dineen killed the wife and kids and then hung himself.

(**EDEL** *sits with this news a moment.*)

EDEL. Did they want him to kill them?

LIAM. I don't know...

EDEL. She had cancer... Julie.

LIAM. I heard that.

EDEL. She gave up the smokes the same time as me...

LIAM. That was probably a good idea.

EDEL. For me, or for her?

LIAM. Good idea in general.

EDEL. No point giving them up now. I've only just started back.

LIAM. I meant the other thing being a good idea...

(*She takes a moment to weigh up what he's saying.*)

EDEL. What are you on about? Him killing them?

LIAM. Well, you said it to me last night.

EDEL. No, I didn't.

> (**EDEL** *stands up and goes over to the counter.*)

LIAM. You did, yeah.

> (**EDEL** *begins pouring some water from a jug into a dirty glass.*)

EDEL. Stop winding me up.

> (**LIAM** *stops his typing and turns to her.*)

LIAM. I'm not winding you up. Honestly.

EDEL. I'm not in the mood.

LIAM. Well, you're the one said it, not me.

EDEL. When did I say it?

LIAM. When we were sitting up above. On the mountain.

EDEL. Said it how?

LIAM. That you thought you'd rather be put out of your misery than keep going through this ordeal of waiting.

EDEL. I was drunk. You know I haven't been drinking for years, I'm just a bit –

LIAM. – it wasn't a bad thing to say in the circumstances Edel, its completely natural –

EDEL. – no, it isn't natural. It's not. I shouldn't have started boozing again.

LIAM. It's understandable in the circumstances.

EDEL. I get dark when I'm drunk, really fucking dark and I thought that mightn't happen anymore, cos it's been years –

LIAM. – stop being so hard on yourself.

EDEL. I was just upset. I'm sorry.

LIAM. I'm just saying... it's an option, as you said yourself.

EDEL. Is it an option?

LIAM. It can be... I suppose.

EDEL. That's how we'll end things, is it? Bullet to the head. Should have put that in the vows.

LIAM. Alright...

EDEL. Until death do us part or put each other out of our absolute fucking misery with a few bullets. There's a great line now. Put that in your memoir. I won't look for a percentage.

LIAM. If it's not how you feel now, that's grand. You're allowed to change your mind about things up until the last second but don't act like we didn't have that conversation.

> (**EDEL** *goes back over to the table and sits down, putting her attention to the laptop.*)

EDEL. Until I say goodbye to my children, I'll be seeing this out, thanks.

LIAM. Well, what I'm saying is that maybe it's not as bad as you think. Whatever way this comes at us, with the fire or –

EDEL. – no. There's enough things here to numb me. It'll go quick, I hope.

> (*They sit there quietly for a few moments. Then:*)

LIAM. I'll plough on so...

> (**LIAM** *goes back to typing.* **EDEL** *just watches him.*)

EDEL. Do you want to do it? Like, for yourself.

LIAM. Well, I'd like to have an option maybe... if it's unbearable, like...

EDEL. Okay...

LIAM. I just don't like seeing people suffering.

EDEL. I'm grand...

> (**EDEL** *begins rolling another cigarette. Then she lights it. A loud droning sound starts outside. Both of them start at the sudden noise. They both get to their feet, anticipating impact. They stare at each other, unsure of what to do. The noise gets louder. Bracing for some sort of crash,* **LIAM** *gets down and scurries under the desk.* **EDEL** *just stands there. She looks up at the ceiling. She braces herself. Then, the noise is gone. And the air is immediately silent again. They both look around. Slowly and ungracefully,* **LIAM** *emerges from under the desk.* **EDEL** *just looks at him, shaking her head, annoyance masked with sarcasm.)*

LIAM. I thought that was it...

EDEL. What a way to go!

LIAM. What?

EDEL. Under the desk. You were willingly going to die under a desk.

LIAM. I didn't know what else to do...

EDEL. I'm sure your bockety wooden desk would have taken all the impact.

> (**LIAM** *isn't in the mood for her taunting. He sits down and returns to his typing.)*

Imagine you now. The last man left on earth, surviving under his shitty old Ikea desk. You could release a whole volume of memoirs. I wonder would you squeeze me under there?

(But **LIAM** *isn't biting.)*

LIAM. Right funny woman until the end...

> **(EDEL** *decides to go over and check in with the laptop again. But there's nothing. Then she starts aimlessly going through her phone. After a few moments,* **LIAM** *stops typing, a thought having struck him.)*

I should have revised the will.

EDEL. Are you serious? Revising the will?

LIAM. This could be a bit of a start over.

EDEL. Do you think?

LIAM. Maybe not for us... I mean... but there's younger people out there who might be able to weather it... somewhere... it'd just be nice to not have all of our stuff go to waste if it could help someone. They could remember us then.

EDEL. Our deaths will matter to literally no one.

LIAM. You don't know that...

EDEL. I'd be more interested in staying than worrying about what's left. Because there's going to be sweet fuck all left when this is done.

> **(LIAM** *goes back to typing.* **EDEL** *walks over to the sink, peering out the window.)*

EDEL. The smoke is getting thicker.

LIAM. What was the first year we ran the charity fundraiser?

EDEL. Clouds of it...

LIAM. Early tens, was it?

EDEL. You can barely see anything.

LIAM. 2013, maybe?

EDEL. What a waste of a gorgeous view.

LIAM. Edel?

EDEL. 2015. Just before Christmas of that year.

LIAM. With Noel and Ellie and Budge and Sarah and...?

EDEL. Wayne...

LIAM. Wayne, that's the lad... what happened to Wayne?

EDEL. He did a runner with the funds... remember?

LIAM. Did he...?

EDEL. Yeah, hundreds from the refugee fund anyway. He was doing it in loads of places, spread about so people wouldn't pick up on it. I think that was his con, going town to town, pretending to work for charities.

LIAM. And he never surfaced again did he?

EDEL. Not after that, no.

LIAM. He was an odd fish.

EDEL. Why do you want to know all this?

>   (**LIAM** *turns around to her.* **EDEL** *turns to him.*)

LIAM. You know those recurring dreams I was telling you about.

EDEL. No.

LIAM. I keep having a recurring dream of getting ready for some event, it feels like one of those fundraisers. Just being in the pub and nothing being ready. None of the mics work, there's loads of people in and I can't find you and everyone is freaking out. It never happened exactly like that in reality but that feeling, y'know? The anticipation of not being ready and all these people just staring you out of it.

EDEL. It's common enough.

LIAM. I thought it might make a nice metaphor.

EDEL. For life?

LIAM. Yeah...

EDEL. We'll never be fully prepared, all that shite. It's a bit done, isn't it?

LIAM. Not done by me. I've my own perspective on it.

EDEL. It's a cliché.

LIAM. When were your happiest times?

> *(The scope of this question seems to wrong foot* **EDEL.** *She thinks a few moments.)*

EDEL. I don't know...

LIAM. I think that might have been it for me. It was around the time we moved out here so it felt fresh, everything was new and it was nice to feel that way when you're a bit older but still young enough to appreciate it. It used to be so much craic in the pubs after, all of us together, seas of friends that just kept coming and you'd never be short on people to talk to or catch up with. Then we'd go for a bag of chips, stagger on home.

EDEL. Yeah... I remember.

LIAM. Felt like years of that.

EDEL. Well, we did it for years.

LIAM. Yeah...

EDEL. There used to be so many more of us back then...

LIAM. All the gang. All dead now... well, I haven't a clue if they're dead or not... who knows at this stage?

EDEL. We don't and we probably won't.

LIAM. Can you think of any happier times we had than that?

EDEL. They're not my memoirs so I don't need to define things like that...

LIAM. They were my happiest times...

EDEL. Were they?

LIAM. They were. I think. *(Pause.)* I think...

EDEL. But in your dreams they're not happy?

LIAM. Not really... just anxious. Then, most recurring dreams are.

EDEL. My recurring dreams aren't.

LIAM. What are they?

EDEL. Ah, the usual stuff.

LIAM. What kind of usual stuff?

EDEL. Nothing that's happened. Not yet.

> (**LIAM** *stops to reread the last thing he typed.* **EDEL** *looks up to the ceiling. She stares at it for a few moments before returning to check her laptop for messages. There's nothing new there so she gets up and stubs out her cigarette. She leaves the room. After a few moments, her voice comes from the hallway.)*

EDEL. *(Offstage.)* You hardly threw out that radio?

LIAM. Which one?

EDEL. *(Offstage.)* That new old one I got you for your fortieth?

LIAM. It's in the attic I think...

> (*There's no response from* **EDEL.** *Just the sound of distant uprooting.*)

(*Louder.*) What do you want it for?

EDEL. (*Offstage.*) There might be people still on it... we might get some news.

LIAM. You'd want to be desperate enough to use that yoke at this point.

EDEL. (*Offstage.*) Says you!

LIAM. Books are real things! They can be kept and tended to.

EDEL. (*Offstage.*) Well it's a good thing you're making the sequel to the Book Of Kells then. I'm sure there'll be scholars tripping over themselves to mind it in the last few minutes of all time. Hope you drew a few nice pictures in there and all. Keep it lively.

> (**LIAM** *ignores her and keeps typing. His phone beeps as a text message arrives. He stops and looks at it for a moment. Then he begins to construct a reply. He sends it. He puts the phone down. He finishes a sentence and pulls a sheet out. With* **EDEL** *outside the room, he takes an opportunity to read through it. He's uncertain, testing the text.*)

LIAM. (*Reading.*) "It was hard to keep writing when the kids were growing up... I'd sneak in an hour or two there which would keep me afloat, but only barely, bobbing away. The life you've chosen is what keeps you from the life you want. But you can't blame anyone. Because in the end, wherever you may be standing, it's all your fault. Everything that happened is your fault. But blame is like a small death in life. And bitterness is a hard cancer to cure". I don't know... hmmmm...

(**LIAM** *muses on his lines. He starts to mutter it through with himself. Then the returning howling of the dog stops him in his tracks.*)

Fuckin' dogs!

(*Then the howling is right outside the back door. The dogs are scraping frantically, wanting to be let in.* **LIAM** *looks over at the gun by the door and contemplates it.*)

EDEL. *(Offstage.)* I got it!

(**LIAM** *gets up and walks over to the gun. He picks it up and checks to see if it's sufficiently loaded. It is. The howling dogs get louder.* **LIAM** *grabs his raincoat off and puts it on. He opens the door.*)

LIAM. Alright! Alright! Fuck up, will ye?! No need for it!

(*The dogs run away from the door but stay barking.* **LIAM** *goes outside, he's just about closing the back door in when his phone starts ringing on the desk. He moves back in quickly and grabs it. He lets it ring out. He realises the door is open. He takes a cursory look outside. He pockets his mobile. He remembers to take the gun. The dogs barking grows louder again.* **LIAM** *leaves, closing the door after him. After he's gone, we hear the dogs barking grow more distant.* **EDEL** *comes back into the room holding an old, dusty radio.*)

EDEL. It's a long shot...

(*She sees that* **LIAM** *is gone. She hears a gunshot. Then* **LIAM** *shouting in the distance. She leaves the radio down on the table and walks over to the door. She opens it and looks*

*outside. She doesn't like what she sees. The
dogs still bark fiercely.)*

(Shouting out.) Do you have to?

LIAM. *(Shouting, offstage.)* They're tormented Edel!

> *(EDEL closes the door after her. She takes a
> deep breath, then she goes over and checks
> her laptop. The dogs get louder. EDEL puts on
> some music to cover the sounds*. Despite this,
> we still hear gunshots ringing out loudly
> from outside. EDEL checks her phone and
> laptop. Then she gets busy setting up the old
> radio on the table. She's fiddling with it as
> LIAM returns from outside, exhausted. There
> are blood splatters on his raincoat. He quickly
> closes the door after him. He puts the gun
> down in the umbrella stand and then begins
> to take off the raincoat. He shakes his head as
> he hangs it back up. EDEL is watching him,
> awaiting some sort of comment. He doesn't
> say anything, just goes back to his typewriter
> and continues typing, a new calm to him.)*

EDEL. Are they dead?

LIAM. Frank is. Joey ran away, I couldn't get him.

EDEL. Poor Joey...

> *(LIAM continues typing, not saying
> anything.)*

I found it.

LIAM. Hmmm...?

---

* A licence to produce DENOUEMENT does not include a performance
licence for any third-party or copyrighted music. Licensees should create
an original composition or use music in the public domain. For further
information, please see Music Use Note on page iii

EDEL. The radio...

LIAM. Does it work?

EDEL. Not sure... they're very impractical. You'd want to have a lot of time on your hands.

> (**LIAM** *continues typing as* **EDEL** *fiddles with the radio. There's nothing but static. Then she reaches one frequency where she can hear a woman crying.* **EDEL** *freezes as the cries begin to fill the room.* **LIAM** *stops typing when he hears it.*)

LIAM. Is that...?

EDEL. Whisht...

LIAM. That's grim enough now...

EDEL. Whisht a second –

LIAM. – don't want to be listening to some mad one bawling for –

EDEL. – whisht to fuck, will you?

> (**LIAM** *is silenced. They listen as the sobbing continues. And then a voice.*)

VOICE. *(On radio.)* There's nobody... nobody telling us what's happening... places are just dropping off, like signal bars on a phone, one by one... no service... if you can hear me... please help us...

EDEL. *(Weakly.)* I can hear you...

> (*But there's no answer. The sobbing continues. Then the voice has died off to be replaced by static.* **LIAM** *goes back to his typing.* **EDEL** *listens for a few moments before moving on to a different frequency.*)

I don't know why these things came back into fashion...

LIAM. Everything came back... our generation was very nostalgic.

EDEL. It's nothing to do with generations. It's just a very particular type of person who is always looking back.

LIAM. When there's nothing ahead of you it's nice to be able to celebrate our past.

EDEL. That's not our past though. Ham radios and typewriters...

LIAM. Well look at where technology got us. The clouds, the electric, the screens... all fucked and now we're back to basics, which we should have done a lot sooner. And I was saying it a very long time –

EDEL. – yeah but you didn't fucking do anything, did you?

LIAM. I refuse to believe that it's never too late to change. You give a good accounting of yourself as best you can up until the end.

EDEL. This. This is it. Here now. The fucking end Liam. I couldn't think of a worse time for looking back on shite.

LIAM. Shur look. That's anniversaries for you.

EDEL. We're arguing in circles.

LIAM. I didn't think we were arguing.

EDEL. What I'm saying, and I'll leave it here, is that just because you're afflicted by nostalgia, it doesn't mean everyone is. I expect you'll want to be buried on a real old school funeral pyre, yeah? Will I just lob you up on a few pallets there in the driveway?

LIAM. If that's what you need to do, then go for it. Just leave flowers for as long as you're around and there's nothing more I'll ask of you. Thanks.

> (**LIAM** *picks up the pace on his typing.* **EDEL** *turns back to radio and begins slowly going through the dial. She listens as faint sounds*

occasionally coming through but mostly just static. Then a voice comes through, quite low, gradually getting louder. EDEL shushes LIAM's typing just as he's getting into a good flow.)

EDEL. There's someone...

(He stops, obviously annoyed at her interruption. EDEL listens intently as the voice becomes clearer. A hushed, eerily calm voice repetitively intoning.)

VOICE. *(On radio.)* The sky is falling... the sky is falling... The sky is falling... The sky is falling... the sky is falling... the sky is falling...

(Then it fades out again. LIAM immediately goes back to his typing. With a new momentum, EDEL keeps scanning through. Music begins to fade up.* EDEL listens to it a while. She begins rolling a cigarette and just quietly sits there. Then the music dies out. EDEL seems disappointed. A thought strikes her as she flicks her cigarette ash on the floor.)

EDEL. Do you think we'll come back?

LIAM. What?

(He barely engages with the answer, he's trying to keep his own momentum going.)

EDEL. Is there a chance we'll come back?

LIAM. Me and you?

EDEL. Not us, no. Humans, I mean.

---

* A licence to produce DENOUEMENT does not include a performance licence for any third-party or copyrighted music. Licensees should create an original composition or use music in the public domain. For further information, please see Music Use Note on page iii

LIAM. Unless the people above in the station can manage something...

EDEL. If they're still up there...

LIAM. If they haven't jumped ship...

EDEL. I'd imagine they'll be stranded.

LIAM. Yeah, just dropping into space. Nothing to orbit around.

EDEL. Floating...

LIAM. Floating... yeah.

EDEL. They should have built on the moon while they had a chance.

LIAM. Hmmm...

EDEL. I wonder if there was some contingency plan we never knew about.

LIAM. Yeah...

EDEL. I mean, it was a long time coming.

LIAM. Edel. I need a bit of quiet for a minute. Just a minute. I'm nearly at the end.

>   (**EDEL** *is quiet for a second. Then:*)

EDEL. Liam?

>   (*He doesn't answer.*)

Liam? (*Pause.*) Liam?!

>   (*He quickly turns to her, annoyed.*)

LIAM. What?

>   (*She very slowly sticks her middle finger up at him.*)

(*Mutters.*) Fuck sake...

(**LIAM** *shakes his head and turns back around. Then his mobile begins ringing. He looks at it. He doesn't answer.*)

EDEL. Aren't you going to answer?

LIAM. No time...

EDEL. Who is it?

LIAM. I have to draw the line at chatting to everyone Edel.

EDEL. Check it.

LIAM. I've too much to get done.

EDEL. It could be Patrick.

LIAM. He wouldn't be ringing me.

EDEL. Just check, will you?

(**LIAM** *takes a cursory look at the phone and then goes back to his typewriter.*)

LIAM. No, it's not...

EDEL. Who is it?

LIAM. I don't know... some random number.

EDEL. Patrick could be ringing on a random number, you numpty.

LIAM. It's not Patrick. It's just people who are too busy dragging out goodbyes and talking shite when they should be focusing on getting through this.

EDEL. Here, let me answer it,

LIAM. Forget it.

EDEL. It might be urgent...

(**EDEL** *walks towards him.* **LIAM** *slams his fist on the desk, hard. It stops her in her tracks.*)

LIAM. It's all urgent Edel! Everything's urgent! Alright? Forget the fucking phones.

> *(He takes a deep breath, composes himself and goes back to typing.* **EDEL** *turns away from him. She returns to the table and begins to tune in the radio some more. After a few moments of scanning, a faint voice materialises with a shipping forecast.)*

VOICE. *(On radio.)* ...heavy rain in the northwest spreading rapidly... *(Static continues.)* Roches Point Automatic...west-southwest, 14 knots, thunder, 8 miles, 1017, rising steadily... Sherkin Island Automatic... west-southwest... 12 knots... cloudy... five miles...

EDEL. I used to love listening to these in bed. *(Leans in as the voice grows fainter.)* I wonder is it an old recording? Imagine there were ships still out there? Kind of like Noah's Ark. You'd have to start somewhere. Someone will do it, I'd bet anything.

> *(Eventually the voice dies away.* **EDEL** *goes through the frequencies looking for another transmission. Another voice materialises through the static.)*

VOICE. *(On radio.)* Mam...? Mam...?

> *(***EDEL** *talks into the radio, her hands shaking slightly.* **LIAM** *stops his typing, listening in.)*

EDEL. Patrick... is that you?

VOICE. *(On radio.)* Mam... can you hear me...?

EDEL. I can hear you...

VOICE. *(On radio.)* ...there hasn't been any contact in days... the sirens have stopped... you can't move for the bodies scattered along the roads...

> *(The static begins to overwhelm the voice.)*

Patrick...? I'm here... I'm here... can you hear me?

(The static returns and the voice disappears.
EDEL *begins to grow more frantic.)*

Patrick? Can you hear me? Patrick? Patrick? Please...
can you hear me?

*(***LIAM*** *gets up from his seat, walks over and
violently sweeps his arm across the table,
sending the radio flying to the floor. It
smashes into pieces.)*

LIAM. It's not him! He's not spending the end of his days
on a fucking ham radio Edel! That wasn't his voice!

*(***EDEL*** *begins to cry.)*

EDEL. How do you know?

LIAM. Because there's no sense in it!

EDEL. What is there sense in? Tell me. If you know so well
what it is we're supposed to be doing?

LIAM. It's just... I know my own son's voice, alright?

EDEL. You haven't talked to him in years.

LIAM. I still remember it.

EDEL. Do you not want to talk to him before it ends?

LIAM. He probably wouldn't want to talk to me.

EDEL. He's your son.

LIAM. He's a mess. And he's the reason we had to move
out here. We could still be living in town, surrounded
by friends and neighbours at a time like this. Instead of
being stuck out here, in the fuckin' sticks.

EDEL. He did his time. He's better now.

*(***LIAM*** *takes a second to calm himself.)*

LIAM. Look, can we not just... can we not just focus on what's here in front of us?

EDEL. By focusing on the past is it?

LIAM. Voices coming out of a banjaxed old radio aren't tangible things Edel. They're probably not even live transmissions, could just be ghost voices from the past. Like the stars shining above in the sky that have been dead for thousands of years, that are still shining.

EDEL. But if they are live transmissions...

LIAM. Why would people be broadcasting during a time like this?

EDEL. They're alone... or stranded... looking for someone to talk to... someone to comfort them...

LIAM. Well, don't you be that sucker Edel. You may as well be sticking messages in bottles at this stage. There are better things you can be doing with the time you have left, alright?

EDEL. Like what? (**LIAM** *doesn't know what to say. He has nothing.*) More drugs... more dancing... another last meal? How many have we had now? What is there left to do only say our goodbyes?

LIAM. I'm wore out with goodbyes.

> (*Then* **LIAM**'s *mobile rings again.* **EDEL** *quickly gets up and goes to go over to it.* **LIAM** *tries to stop her. She slaps his hands away.*)

Edel!

EDEL. Fuck off Liam.

LIAM. For fuck... sake.

> (**EDEL** *answers his mobile.*)

EDEL. (*Into phone.*) Hello?

LIAM. Edel, now...

EDEL. *(Into phone.)* Yeah. Who's this?

> *(The call goes dead. **LIAM** grabs the phone back off her.)*

LIAM. What do you want me to do? Do you want me to try Patrick? I'll do it if that's what you want.

EDEL. Who was that?

LIAM. How do I know?

EDEL. You do know.

LIAM. There isn't a moments peace, is there?

EDEL. It sounded like Una.

> *(**LIAM** hesitates for a moment.)*

LIAM. Look, people want comfort at the end, it's no different to –

> *(Then there's a loud knock on their door. **EDEL** jumps. **LIAM** immediately grabs her by the shoulders to stop her moving. He mimes for her to be quiet. They stand there together, held, entirely still. There's another knock Then silence.)*

EDEL. *(Quietly, miming.)* Who's that?

> *(**LIAM** says nothing, just gestures for her to not talk. Then **LIAM**'s mobile rings again. He jumps with the noise. He quickly turns it off, as quietly as he can. They wait a few moments. Then a woman's voice can be heard shouting outside. "Liam!".)*

LIAM. For fuck sake...

EDEL. Is it her?

LIAM. She keeps messaging me, keeps ringing me... the past few days...

*(**EDEL** grabs the shotgun from its place and beelines over to the back door.)*

No, Edel! Don't, it's not safe... Edel?

(But it's too late, she's opened it. She looks out a second and goes out into the yard.)

Bollocks...

*(**LIAM** paces a bit, no idea what to do. Then he slowly moves over and peers outside to see where **EDEL** has gone. He walks back in, leaving the door open. He stands aimlessly by the kitchen table. Then **EDEL** returns, leaving the door open. She puts the gun down.)*

EDEL. She's parked up on the road. She's pacing about the place. She doesn't seem well... not by any means.

LIAM. Did she see you?

EDEL. No...

LIAM. How bad is she?

EDEL. Oh, about as well as you'd expect. But then, I don't know what you were expecting.

LIAM. I don't want to talk to her...

EDEL. Well, she wants to talk to you.

LIAM. I think she's lost it Edel.

EDEL. How do you think that?

LIAM. She's erratic, like... been sending me mad messages.

EDEL. You could have told me.

LIAM. You've had enough to be worrying about.

EDEL. Did we not agree to be open with each other about everything? After the last time?

LIAM. We did but... you never account for the end of the world, y'know?

*(**LIAM** goes over and circles the back door, trying to see if he can spot the woman. **EDEL** is controlling her anger but she's not letting him get away from her so easily.)*

EDEL. Death is death... it makes no difference if we're all going at the same time or if we're not.

LIAM. I don't want to waste the last of my time dealing with her.

EDEL. Well she wants to spend the last of hers with you.

LIAM. That's her bad luck.

EDEL. You going to leave a hysterical woman out there in that state?

LIAM. I don't know how to get rid of her.

*(A silence hangs in the air. **EDEL** is weighing it up. Then she goes for it.)*

EDEL. Has it been going on again?

LIAM. Are you seriously asking me that?

EDEL. If it has now's the time to tell me.

LIAM. It hasn't.

EDEL. Because there's absolutely no point in lying now.

LIAM. Edel, I swear nothing has happened. I've barely talked to her in years. Only a wave out on the road or the smallest of talk in town but that's the height of it.

EDEL. Her showing up to our house like this wouldn't instil me with confidence.

LIAM. I told you the truth about everything.

EDEL. After I found out.

LIAM. It was a very different time.

EDEL. Are you getting nostalgic?

LIAM. Ah here...

EDEL. You always said she was the kind of woman you thought you'd end up with it.

LIAM. Years ago!

EDEL. You said it.

LIAM. Yeah, when I was drunk. Talking shit.

EDEL. That's when the truth comes out with you.

LIAM. Like when you said you'd rather a bullet in the head and end on your own terms?

> (**EDEL** *says nothing. She just stares through him.* **LIAM** *changes tack.*)

This isn't the time for this... she just... she lives alone Edel.

EDEL. I don't care if she's alone, fuck her, that's where her open relationships got her.

LIAM. How scary do you think this must be for someone on their own?

EDEL. What do you think I am Liam?

LIAM. I'm here.

EDEL. What difference does that make?

LIAM. I mean... she's probably terrified... she doesn't have anyone.

EDEL. Do you want to let her in?

LIAM. Do you?

EDEL. What the fuck do you think?

(From outside, a woman's voice shouting **LIAM**'s *name. Silence for a second, then more shouting.)*

I'm not listening to her out there. No way. I am not finishing like this.

*(**EDEL** walks back to her laptop and checks it. **LIAM** watches her.)*

LIAM. Edel? I don't want to go out...

EDEL. I deserve to live the last of my time without her crowing outside my house. It's your mess. Sort it out.

*(**LIAM** watches her, he's unsure of what to do.)*

LIAM. Alright. I'll go... I'll tell her to go home... alright?

*(**EDEL** doesn't say anything. **LIAM**'s mobile starts ringing again. **LIAM** watches **EDEL** for a moment but she doesn't pay him any attention. Then he turns and picks up the shotgun. He walks out the door, leaving it open. When he's gone, **EDEL** gets up and goes over. She looks outside to see what's happening. When there's no sign of either of them, she slams the door shut. She walks back to the table. She picks up her own mobile. She scrolls through the contacts. She hesitates a few seconds. Then she rings a number. It rings for a while with no answer before going to voicemail. **EDEL** hesitates for a few more seconds. Then:)*

EDEL. *(Into phone.)* Hi Cian... it's Edel here... I hope you're keeping well... Well, I hope you're still alive. Grim way to begin. Sorry. Anyway, look... I know this might be out of the blue but with everything that's been going on and... I just want you to know that if you're still open to... what we talked about before, I suppose. I know it's been a few years. But last night I saw you up above at the vigil or session or whatever you call it and there was a bit of... eye contact with us I suppose and well, we haven't... I don't think we've looked at each other like that... for years. Maybe, if you're still interested or if you're up for it or whatever, whatever you think, like, you know, maybe you want to meet up before whatever's about to happen, if you're into it. *(Pause.)* If you want. *(Pause.)* It does funny things to you, doesn't it? The end...

> *(She puts the mobile back down. She goes back to the laptop. She rolls up a cigarette. Then there's a gunshot outside.* **EDEL** *gives a start. She goes over to the back door and opens it. She lights the cigarette. She stares outside for a few moments until we hear footsteps coming towards the door.* **LIAM** *comes back in, blood splattered all over him. He's impassive, blank. He puts the shotgun down.)*

LIAM. She's gone.

> *(He goes over to the kitchen sink and begins to clean himself.)*

EDEL. What happened?

LIAM. She wanted me to go with her... to stay with her for the rest of it.

EDEL. And?

LIAM. I told her it was all done with and... I just said my goodbyes and... she wouldn't let me go... I was pulling hard away from her.

> *(This settles for a moment as* **LIAM** *continues cleaning blood off himself.)*

EDEL. Did you shift her?

LIAM. Did I shift her? Am I just after coming back in from a teen fuckin' disco, am I?

EDEL. Kiss... did you kiss her?

(**LIAM** *pauses for a moment, then he nods.*)

You kissed her there, just outside there now...

LIAM. I hugged her and she went to kiss me and I kissed her back... a peck was all. In the moment, just to... reassure her I suppose... something to comfort her. As I was walking away, she took out this gun and called my name. I tried to stop her but...

EDEL. ...but what?

LIAM. She shot herself in the head.

(**LIAM** *goes to the table and begins cutting up another line of coke.* **EDEL** *watches him. He snorts it up, quickly.* **EDEL** *stubs her cigarette out on the floor.*)

EDEL. I'm glad she's dead...

LIAM. I bet you are...

EDEL. I hope it hurt.

LIAM. Alright now...

EDEL. Like, I hope there were a few seconds after she'd shot herself where she was able to realise it, feel the pain, like –

LIAM. – please stop.

EDEL. That she'd even try to pull a stroke like that at the end of it all...

LIAM. Well, she's at peace now...

EDEL. With her head blown off lying at the end of our driveway... yeah, some fucking peace that is. It's more pieces she's in than anything else.

LIAM. What do you want me to say?

EDEL. You're not able to say anything are you? Nothing of comfort, nothing of any use or reassurance. Nothing of any substance at all.

LIAM. I am trying my best...

EDEL. Your best is the worst. Even now. You couldn't comfort a hysterical woman without her blowing her brains out. That's how much use your words are. She'd rather shoot herself in the head than listen to your shite anymore.

LIAM. That's not fair...

EDEL. Go back to your memoirs cos you're not worth a fuck at anything else...

> (**LIAM** *walks back over to the typewriter and begins to type furiously.* **EDEL** *watches him go, with barely disguised disdain.* **EDEL** *begins the routine of rolling up another cigarette. After a few moments, the sound of an incoming call comes onto the laptop.* **EDEL** *quickly answers.)*

Mairead!

> *(She adjusts the screen. Turns up the speakers.)*

Mairead!

MAIREAD. *(On screen.)* Mam!

EDEL. Oh, it's so good to hear your voice.

MAIREAD. *(On screen.)* Oh, you too. I didn't think I'd get a chance to talk to you.

EDEL. Me neither...

MAIREAD. *(On screen.)* How are you?

EDEL. Not too bad love, all things considering.

> (**LIAM** *keeps hammering away on the typewriter.*)

LIAM. *(As he types.)* "If life has taught me anything" *(Pauses. Scratches his nose.)* Finish your memoirs before the fucking apocalypse.

MAIREAD. *(On screen.)* Are you and Da alright? Are you still at home?

> *(Suddenly there's the sound of a dog outside. Barking loudly and scraping the door.)*

EDEL. Sorry love, I can't hear you. The dogs are going mad here.

LIAM. Fuck this. Fuck this!

> (**LIAM** *quickly gets up off his chair, goes over and grabs the gun. He disappears outside.*)

EDEL. How's everyone?

MAIREAD. *(On screen.)* They're grand ma. They're prepared for the worst. Niamh is here.

EDEL. Oh, let me talk to her.

MAIREAD. *(On screen.)* Just to let you know, we told her... we kind of had to tell her, it's been going on so long.

EDEL. Oh, okay... how did she –

MAIREAD. *(On screen.)* – say hello to granny Niamh.

NIAMH. *(Offstage.)* Hi granny!

EDEL. Hello Niamh! How are you?

NIAMH. *(Offstage/Cheerily.)* We're all going to die Granny!

EDEL. Well love, if that's what we're doing, we'll be doing it all together.

(Gunshots outside. Howling. Another gunshot. Silence.)

MAIREAD. *(On screen.)* What was that?

EDEL. I think your father was just... taking Joey to the farm.

MAIREAD. *(On screen.)* Ah no...

NIAMH. *(Offstage.)* But you live on a farm Granny?

> **(LIAM** *quickly re-enters with a shotgun and slams the door shut. He lays the gun down.)*

EDEL. Grandad was taking him to a different kind of farm love.

LIAM. The farm means they're dead love. No point dressing it up now. Your Grandad had to kill the dogs. They were too upset and it was for the best.

MAIREAD. *(On screen.)* Jesus, Da!

NIAMH. *(Offstage.)* Grandad killed the dogs?

LIAM. *(Protesting, to* **MAIREAD.***)* It was a mercy killing!

EDEL. *(To* **LIAM,** *quieting him.)* Shut up will you? Niamh is there.

NIAMH. *(Offstage.)* Where's Grandad gone?

EDEL. He'll be back over in a second...

> **(LIAM** *sits back down at the typewriter and starts clacking away again.)*

MAIREAD. *(On screen.)* Are there many alive near you?

EDEL. Yeah, yeah. There's a few still intact.

MAIREAD. *(On screen.)* A lot of our neighbours are gone already mam.

EDEL. How did ye escape that?

MAIREAD. *(On screen.)* No, they went themselves, y'know? Rather than wait for it, like.

EDEL. There's a lot of that going around these parts too love. *(Pause.)* Are you going to see it out?

MAIREAD. *(On screen.)* Yeah... yeah... I think so mam. But we're not sure about the kids. They'd be so scared. They could be. I don't know. So we might... we were thinking, like...

EDEL. I know. I know love. Don't... you're not doing anything wrong.

MAIREAD. *(On screen, upset.)* Am I not?

EDEL. All bets are off.

MAIREAD. *(On screen.)* Thanks... sorry, you never consider you're going to have conversations like this.

EDEL. No, not these kind of conversations. It's a lot of goodbyes to get through.

MAIREAD. *(On screen.)* Yeah. Trying to leave everything on as light a note as possible.

EDEL. Eulogising.

MAIREAD. *(On screen.)* I'm wore out with it...

EDEL. It's the waiting that'd kill you...

MAIREAD. *(On screen.)* Did Patrick ring you?

EDEL. No, did he ring you?

MAIREAD. *(On screen.)* He got me a few hours ago, he was on someone else's phone. Squashed into an apartment with a few others, they only just managed to get up there. He said the streets were a write off.

EDEL. Oh good! Oh... that's a relief.

MAIREAD. *(On screen.)* He said he couldn't get through to you...

EDEL. We were up at the... vigil... party... whatever you fucking call it.

MAIREAD. *(On screen.)* Look, don't be worrying.

EDEL. It's hard to keep track of all the unknown numbers. Phone was hopping for ages.

MAIREAD. *(On screen.)* Yeah, he said people were killing each other to get working phones.

EDEL. Oh...

MAIREAD. *(On screen.)* Well, hopefully he was one of the lucky ones. There's still time.

EDEL. I hope so. *(Shouts over.)* Liam!

LIAM. Sorry... sorry...

> (**LIAM** *moves away from the typewriter and goes to the laptop.*)

EDEL. Here he is now, gracing us...

LIAM. Well love... how are ye?

EDEL. Bend down there so she can see you properly.

> (**LIAM** *does, gingerly, squeezing in next to* **EDEL***. We can hear* **MAIREAD** *crying.*)

LIAM. Ah don't cry love, don't cry.

MAIREAD. *(On screen.)* Sorry Da, it's just...

LIAM. There's Keith there now.

KEITH. *(Offstage.)* Hi folks.

EDEL. Hi Keith.

LIAM. Well Keith, looking after the girls are you?

MAIREAD. *(On screen.)* We're all looking after each other Da.

KEITH. *(Offstage.)* They're in good hands. You folks take caring of yourselves?

EDEL. Just tying up the loose ends.

LIAM. Have a bit of steak defrosting for the dinner too so fingers crossed.

KEITH. *(Offstage.)* Nice to be able to eat it again, isn't it?

LIAM. Special occasion man. Any plans yourselves?

KEITH. *(Offstage.)* We had a very stacked barbecue this morning. Might have another one... if there's time.

LIAM. A good idea.

KEITH. *(Offstage.)* Yeah, just use up the last of the stuff. Lot of people brought meat.

LIAM. Good, good. The meat won't last anyway. Not in your climate anyway.

KEITH. *(Offstage.)* Oh yeah, absolute scorcher here today.

LIAM. Ah, that's something anyway. *(Pause. A slight silence.)* Oh! Keith?

KEITH. *(Offstage.)* Yeah?

LIAM. I just want you to know how much I like you. I always thought you mightn't think that because I got on so well with Mairead's last fella but you're the best man I could have given her away to. I honestly mean that now.

KEITH. *(Offstage.)* Thanks Liam, she's the best woman I could have been given...

MAIREAD. *(On screen.)* Alright, less of the given talk. I went where I wanted.

KEITH. *(Offstage.)* Yeah, just don't go having any last minute regrets.

MAIREAD. *(On screen)* Ah, I'm having loads of them but what's the point now.

> *(We can hear them share a laugh.* **EDEL** *laughs along with them.)*

LIAM. And Mairead, can you remember which year we went to Amsterdam? When you were small?

MAIREAD. *(On screen.)* Twenty six wasn't it?

LIAM. Twenty six...

MAIREAD. *(On screen.)* During the World Cup...

LIAM. That was it... great times.

MAIREAD. *(On screen.)* They were.

LIAM. Mairead, you're the best thing that ever happened to me and I know you won't get to read my memoirs but there's a bit where I say that every bit of hassle you caused me and every bit of heartbreak was worth it. There were dark days that the thoughts of you would get me through and I don't think I'd be here without you. That's the jist of it anyway.

MAIREAD. *(On screen.)* Thanks Da... thanks for being so good to me.

LIAM. Thanks love...

MAIREAD. *(On screen.)* You don't know how glad I am to get through to ye...

> *(***EDEL** *starts crying.* **LIAM** *doesn't do much to comfort her. He just stands awkwardly.)*

(On screen.) Just please, take care of yourselves.

LIAM. And you too love. Mind your mammy and daddy won't you Niamh?

NIAMH. *(Offstage.)* Yes Grandad!

MAIREAD. *(On screen.)* I love you both.

EDEL. *(Offstage.)* I love you too.

LIAM. And so do I.

MAIREAD. *(On screen.)* Niamh, say bye to your granny and –

> *(An explosion rings out from outside. Louder than any previous. The feed goes dead.* **LIAM** *and* **EDEL** *stare at it.* **EDEL** *is trying to reconnect but there's nothing.)*

EDEL. Ah no. No...

LIAM. That's it Edel, it's not coming back. They're not coming back.

EDEL. Oh Jesus...

LIAM. I don't think we're going to get much more out of that reactor.

> *(***LIAM*** *frenetically begins cutting out a huge line of cocaine.* **EDEL** *walks away from him and grabs a wine bottle.* **EDEL** *goes to pour a glass but nothing comes out. It's empty.)*

EDEL. Did we drink everything?

LIAM. Finished it this morning.

> *(***LIAM*** *hoovers up the line of coke. He lets out a charged roar. Then shakes it off. He's moving forward, ready for the final rally.)*

EDEL. Nothing left in the attic?

LIAM. No... nothing. Not a drop.

EDEL. *(Roaring.)* FUCK IT!

> *(In frustration,* **EDEL** *throws the bottle through the hallway door. We hear it smash against a wall.* **LIAM** *flinches at the noise.* **EDEL** *is shaking. He's not sure what to say*

to her. He gestures towards the drugs on the table.)

LIAM. Do you want any...?

(EDEL slowly walks over and slumps down on the armchair.)

EDEL. I've had enough. I've just... had enough. I just want this to end...

LIAM. It won't be long Edel...

EDEL. They're gone... our children...

LIAM. Yeah... I...

(She puts her head in her hands and begins to sob quietly. LIAM puts a hand to her shoulder, gingerly. She shrugs it off. Her crying intensifies. He looks over towards the shotgun. He walks over and gently takes it. He seems unsure of himself, uncertain. He walks over behind EDEL. He wipes his nose, still sniffling from the cocaine. EDEL isn't aware of him behind her. She sits with her head in her hands, bereft.)

EDEL. Our children... our children...

(LIAM is finding it hard to stay composed. As gently as he can, he begins to raise the gun up before pointing it at the back of her head. EDEL still isn't minding him. Then suddenly, another explosion outside, closer, more violent. EDEL jumps up suddenly. LIAM drops the shotgun on the floor, with a clatter. He momentarily jolts, thinking it might go off. But it doesn't. EDEL doesn't notice it. She's looking towards the ceiling.)

EDEL. Wait. This is it... now...

LIAM. No...

(He rushes back over to the typewriter and begins frantically hammering at it.)

I have to finish... I have to finish...

(The sounds of destruction and chaos rage outside in the near distance. **EDEL** *moves with a renewed urgency. She grabs her phone and makes a phone call. It just rings out again. She puts the phone back down. After a few aimless seconds, she turns up the music on the laptop*. Something to cover the noise from outside. She sees the shotgun lying there and contemplates it a second. Then she picks it up. She walks over and puts it right back where it was. She grabs a sweeping brush and dustpan. She begins sweeping up the broken remnants of the radio from the floor.* **LIAM** *slows down the pace of his typing to talk to her.)*

Are you still talking to me?

EDEL. Who else am I going to talk to?

LIAM. You were angry with me.

EDEL. You tell me that I'm always angry with you.

LIAM. I thought you didn't want to listen to old music anymore?

EDEL. I just don't want to listen to that clusterfuck outside.

LIAM. This song was playing in the car when we brought Mairead back from the hospital, remember?

---

* A licence to produce DENOUEMENT does not include a performance licence for any third-party or copyrighted music. Licensees should create an original composition or use music in the public domain. For further information, please see Music Use Note on page iii

EDEL. And she'd just gone asleep...

LIAM. Yeah...

EDEL. Yeah...

> (**EDEL** *is putting the broken bits into the bin.*
> *She stands over by the sink, looking at what's*
> *happening outside.* **LIAM***'s writing flow peters*
> *out. He's stuck on something.*)

LIAM. Do you regret not having more children?

EDEL. Why are you asking that?

LIAM. I wrote it down and I wanted to know what you thought.

EDEL. You wrote down what?

LIAM. That I regretted not having more.

EDEL. You wanted more?

LIAM. I think I would have liked one or two more, yeah.

EDEL. One you haven't spoken to in years and another I had to drag your arse over here to say goodbye to and you would have liked one or two more?

LIAM. Ah here, that's not fair.

EDEL. What isn't fair?

LIAM. Mairead. We always got on. I know the two of ye used to kill each other but we got on great. For the most part.

EDEL. And two more would have made all the difference to your happiness would it?

LIAM. Stop being so passive aggressive.

EDEL. I'm not...

LIAM. All I'm saying, in my memoirs like, is that the two of them don't even live in the country... would have been nice to have family here with us at the end.

EDEL. Yeah, and you wouldn't say shit to them because you'd be too busy typing your memoirs.

> (**LIAM** *stops typing. He turns around to face her.*)

LIAM. What do you want me to do? You tell me what you want and I'll do it Edel. I'll stop typing this second if there's something you want me to do. The only reason I'm writing this shit down is because everything else is done.

EDEL. It's not done yet.

LIAM. Well, as good as.

EDEL. You make only a small handful of big decisions ever and then you're here, about to die. That's it. And you end up regretting all the time in between that you wasted on shite. Like your memoirs. So just... do something that's a bit forward thinking maybe.

> (**LIAM** *turns and goes back to his typing.* **EDEL** *watches him a second, then:*)

I do wish I'd had another one.

> (**LIAM** *stops immediately. He turns to her.*)

LIAM. A child?

EDEL. Yeah. To answer your question.

LIAM. Why?

EDEL. I think I would have done it better the third time. That's all.

> (*As she's bending back over to sweep, the holy medal falls out from under her cardigan.*)

(**LIAM** *sees it. She quickly tucks it back in.*)

LIAM. You wearing a holy medal?

> (*She doesn't say anything, she continues with her sweeping, trying to ignore him.*)

(*Laughs.*) Having a come to God moment, are we?

> (**EDEL** *stops what she's doing. She's angry.*)

EDEL. Fuck off with yourself, alright?

LIAM. And you think I'm wasting my time...

EDEL. I don't know what else to do.

LIAM. You don't have to clean up... why are you cleaning up?

EDEL. If you thought there was some way to stop this would you not try?

LIAM. Is that why you want me to stop writing... so I can pray?

EDEL. I didn't say pray, just... anything that might help.

LIAM. The church is dead and gone Edel. Don't fall for that shit right at the end. There's enough fuckin' saps already doing that.

EDEL. There's worse things people could be doing at the end.

LIAM. Yeah, and we've avoided it haven't we?

EDEL. Avoided what?

LIAM. We must be one of the only ones round here not to poison ourselves or hang ourselves or blow our bloody brains out.

EDEL. And why didn't we?

LIAM. I wanted to finish this. I can't speak for you.

(There's a pause between them. The noise from beyond fills the room. **LIAM** *is looking at* **EDEL** *but she's not returning it.)*

If you want to go... before it happens... I can do it... I can. You just tell me.

*(***EDEL*** *isn't saying anything, she's staring at the floor.* **LIAM** *turns back to his typewriter as if to type. He's quietly awaiting her response. Before he can start typing,* **EDEL** *speaks. He doesn't turn back to her. He talks as he types.)*

EDEL. We just thought we'd be grand, didn't we? That we'd miss out on the worst of it, that we'd be dead and comfortably buried in the ground before –

LIAM. – we're being punished are we? By God? Is that it?

EDEL. No, just... why has it happened now and not ever before?

LIAM. It was going to happen at some point Edel.

EDEL. It didn't need to happen now...

LIAM. Easy to say with hindsight.

EDEL. We could have gotten a few more years out of it, easily.

LIAM. We're only lodgers here. That's all we are. Even if this is our fault, religion wasn't going to help us. It never helped us before so why would it help us now?

EDEL. Because it's the end now.

LIAM. You may give over because if we get wiped out now in a second I don't want religion to be the last thing I talked about.

EDEL. I wish it had happened earlier. At a better time. We could have avoided all that anxiety.

LIAM. It is what it is and we do what we can...

EDEL. Every single decision, the big ones, the small ones... they all caught up with us. We let it get to this point. And look at the shit we're in.

> (**LIAM** *stops typing. He makes to turn to her but then doesn't. He puts his hand back on the typewriter.*)

LIAM. You're the one who didn't want to be looking into the past...

EDEL. I'm not, I'm just wondering if there's any way we can still fix it.

> (**LIAM** *stays still for a few more seconds.* **EDEL** *watches the back of his head, anticipating him doing something. Then he resumes typing.* **EDEL**'s *mobile starts ringing. She grabs it and looks to see who it is. She walks to the other corner of the room. Then she answers.*)

(Into phone.) Hello... How are you? *(Pause.)* I'm sorry for the call... *(Pause.)* No, no, you're grand. *(Pause.)* Did she? *(Pause.)* No, shit... I didn't want to cause any upset... I didn't know she would... *(Pause.)* Look, I don't think anyone is thinking straight at a time like this. *(Pause.)* You didn't have to ring if that was the case. *(Pause.)* I didn't do it on purpose. (Pause) There's no need to talk to me like that... come on... *(Pause. A flash of anger across her face.)* Yeah, well... hope you die screaming. *(Pause.)* Ah, go fuck yourself.

> (*Then she hangs up, angrily but accidentally drops the phone. It falls on the ground and smashes.* **EDEL** *stands, frozen, staring at the smashed phone.* **LIAM** *keeps on typing, not minding her. He mutters to himself as he continues hammering the words out.* **EDEL** *just stands there, bereft.*)

LIAM. *(Muttering, barely audible.)* "You can lose all sense of everything... but the most important thing to keep hold of is sense itself..."

> *(Then, **LIAM**'s mobile rings. He jumps with a fright from the sudden sound.)*

(Agitated.) Ah, bollocks. *(Looks at phone.)* Here Edel, answer this. Edel?

> *(**EDEL** is just standing there, staring at her broken phone. She doesn't move.)*

Edel? Fuck sake... *(He answers.)* Hello? *(Pause.)* Patrick? *(Pause.)* Yeah. I'm here. *(Pause.)* I'm sorry. *(Pause.)* I love you too.

> *(Then there's nothing. **LIAM** listens for a further second but it's gone dead. He puts his phone down.)*

EDEL. Patrick?

LIAM. He's gone.

EDEL. Gone?

LIAM. Something had... I think it's gone... London...

EDEL. Oh Jesus, Patrick... oh Jesus...

LIAM. A few screams and it... went dead.

EDEL. At least you told him that you...

LIAM. It's done now. Forget it.

EDEL. I didn't get to tell him... say a goodbye or...

LIAM. Forget it...

EDEL. How was he?

LIAM. He sounded... I don't know... elated, maybe?

EDEL. Okay... okay...

(**LIAM** *starts hammering away at the typewriter again.* **EDEL** *stands there blankly.* **LIAM** *is murmuring under his breath. The noises outside get louder.* **EDEL** *looks up to the ceiling again.*)

Is that what déjà vu is I wonder? Something that's already planted in your head coming to pass.

(**LIAM** *doesn't answer her. He keeps typing frenetically.*)

We never did figure it out, did we?

(*Then he slams his fists down on the typewriter in frustration.*)

LIAM. *(Muttering.)* Come on...

EDEL. Recurring dreams, I mean...

(**EDEL** *takes the holy medal out from under her clothes again. She prays silently.* **LIAM** *keeps typing, his pace steadily increasing.*)

LIAM. Yes... *(Starts slowing down.)* yes... *(Slowing down.)* and...

(*Then he hits one last button. He stops.*)

Done! I'm done.

(*He collapses his head into his hands. He takes a deep breath.*)

EDEL. *(Barely audible.)* Amen.

(**LIAM** *regroups as quick as he can. He takes the last page out and places it on a pile. He takes a large paper clip and fastens it to the bundle. Then he sits back on his chair, staring at it.* **EDEL** *stays standing, staring ahead blankly. There is silence between them* *for about thirty seconds. The noise outside has subsided. An eerie silence permeates.)*

(They both stare ahead aimlessly, absorbed in uncertainty. Then:)

I was thinking about leaving you...

*(**LIAM** slowly turns to her.)*

LIAM. When?

EDEL. Years ago... and now... today.

LIAM. Who?

EDEL. Cian Howley. That was who was on the phone there. I called him and left him a voicemail and... I'm a careless bitch... right until the end...

LIAM. You'd leave me for him?

EDEL. But I didn't.

LIAM. That cunt? The head on him up there last night, wouldn't even say a nice word to me and it the end of the world. He blanked me, the cunt.

EDEL. He flirted with me for years. When we'd be down the town on nights out or at weddings or he'd drop into the studio every so often when I was working. And then messages for years. And it had a flirty edge to it but in a harmless way. And then one night, this is maybe, twenty years ago, we were at a party in Cillian and Sarah's house... when they used to have the bands out the back, remember? And you were drunk, talking to Budge and Holly about your regrets... becoming a teacher, staying a teacher, settling too soon when everyone else was settling later, the usual things you were talking about when you were drunk and melancholy at that time. I was wore out with you. He was flirting with me and I was enjoying it. But it just got a bit full on... not touching or anything but it was beyond the boundaries of what would be acceptable. And I was wasted... like, this was when my drinking started getting really bad. But the party was getting messy anyway. Everyone was being scaldy with each other. Groping and bits of kissing. I was going to the bathroom... but as I did, I gave him this wink or a nod maybe... a nod to urge him to join me... and I went to the smaller bathroom in their spare bedroom... and I waited. And in my head he was going to come in and we were going to fuck... that was what was going to happen and I was ready. He'd come in and we'd fuck quickly and no one would notice a thing and then we'd just go back to the party. This was around that time where people really started to question monogamy I suppose. Everything was really fluid and all these open relationships were going on. But I started to get butterflies in my stomach and then it just... I just had this very sober, glaring moment where I looked at myself in the mirror and saw what a mess I was. And I was going to leave when there was a knock at the door. And I opened it and Cian was there. And I made some kind of joke 'It's all yours' or something... and he just pushed me back in. And he started kissing me, feeling me up. I resisted it. I apologised for leading him on and I was sorry. And he didn't force anything as soon as I said that. But he told me that he'd leave his wife for me in a heartbeat if it ever came to it. And for months after, he'd still message me and say the same thing. He said he hated his wife, couldn't stand his kids. But I could never do that... I just thought of you and our kids and I just couldn't do that to you. And I was proud of myself in a way for resisting it. I was ashamed for letting it get to that point but maybe... I was testing myself. My commitment to you. And it worked. And I felt the happiest I had in years. And then you left me for her.

(**LIAM** *takes all of this in. After a few moments, an explosion rings out in the distance.*)

LIAM. I came back.

EDEL. But you left. When the going got tough.

LIAM. You seemed so distant from me.

EDEL. I was... and I started to stray but then I stopped myself.

LIAM. I couldn't...

EDEL. Did you write about that?

LIAM. I did. And how it fucked up my life. And I wrote that she shot herself in the head not an hour ago and I had to clean her brains off my clothes. *(Realises.)* I need to change these clothes... I can't die wearing her brains...

> (**LIAM** *urgently gets up and begins to take his clothes off his shirt and trousers. He pulls a dirty t-shirt and a pair of jeans from the basket. As he gets dressed again, they talk.*)

EDEL. I don't know what I was thinking ringing him... no, that's not true, I do. I don't want to die alone.

LIAM. You're not alone. I know I've been preoccupied –

EDEL. – you've been preoccupied for twenty-nine years.

LIAM. And you spent most of their childhood looking at your phone.

EDEL. Well, I'm sorry that you didn't like your life.

LIAM. That's not true.

EDEL. That it got ruined...

LIAM. No, it nearly did. But it didn't.

EDEL. Okay.

(They both nod at this. They're accepting each other's points. The silence settles again. LIAM *walks a few steps closer to her.)*

LIAM. I thought I had time to make sense of it.

EDEL. What?

LIAM. My life... our life. Get the bullet points of what was important. Because it's hard to see what's important when you're in it, you know?

EDEL. What's important?

LIAM. Well, you.

EDEL. What's important about me?

LIAM. I told you all this last night. Well, the night before, whatever that was.

EDEL. We've been up since... this is, what day is this?

LIAM. No look, I'm saying I told you everything I feel that night. We had a lovely chat. I thought, anyway.

EDEL. When?

LIAM. After I tucked you into bed.

EDEL. I can't remember.

LIAM. We were just nattering away. Holding hands like two little otters, so we wouldn't get swept away. Like we used to. And I told you all this and you said you didn't believe me.

EDEL. You were drunk. And high.

LIAM. Yeah, so what? I can still be truthful can't I?

EDEL. I can't remember much of it is all... I haven't been that drunk in...

LIAM. I know. But it came up anyway.

EDEL. I was half asleep.

LIAM. As far as I was concerned it was all said...

> *(They both stand there, uncertainly for a moment. Black smoke starts to sweep past the window. The sound of distant destruction is getting louder. It's getting closer.)*

EDEL. That vigil would have been nice... I don't think it's happening now...

LIAM. You're still holding out for something better than me, are you?

EDEL. It would have been nice to have everyone together at the end is all...

LIAM. Focus on the horrible times if you want. That way you won't miss me...

EDEL. I don't want to do that.

LIAM. I'm sorry I disappointed you so much. I disappointed myself.

EDEL. You can't think like that... not now. I'm not trying to make you feel guilty. I just want to get it all off my chest. I just wish I felt happier when everything was at its best. And I wish I felt less alone than I do now.

> *(There's a loud noise from outside, closer than before. It's coming. The urgency propels.)*

> *(**LIAM** to get it all out, whatever he has left.)*

LIAM. Marie, who I was with before you... she got pregnant and I insisted she get an abortion and I paid for it. Brought her to England... back when you had to do that. She was unsure about it all the way over and I just... I couldn't have a babby messing up my life... not then. And she cried for weeks after. I don't think she ever stopped crying. I knew I'd ruined that relationship... and she was scarred by it. In a way you wouldn't come back from. She was a shell. And I left her too. Zero fucks given. She never had children after. I remember seeing on Facebook that she'd died in Scotland. She was found in her flat four weeks after she died and I thought to myself that it wouldn't have happened if our baby was there to mind her.

EDEL. Stop this. It'll be here soon...

LIAM. I took a rake of coke with Patrick on his twenty first. I even bought it for him and he collapsed in a heap outside the club and I thought I was after killing him. I spent all night minding him, terrified of what you'd do if you found out. The next day we swore never to tell you. And I often thought for a long time that it was my fault he got hooked on drugs and went off the rails... and if he hadn't he wouldn't have driven that car like he did and killed that poor Delaney girl.

EDEL. Don't try and make me hate you...

LIAM. And I got arrested once, when I went on a stag with the lads, I got done for drink driving and spent a night in the cells in Ennis and they kept me there much longer than they should because I took a piss in the corner. I rang the guards on Shane Welsh too. I was the one who told them he was selling guns and then... they took him away and he had young kids and it ruined him in town but he took credit for my work and he was a prick so I... I was a spiteful bastard at my worst. But I could never tell you how spiteful I was.

EDEL. Give over.

LIAM. What else... what else...

EDEL. Enough.

> (LIAM *deliberates a few seconds. Then he says it.*)

LIAM. And I was nearly going to shoot you a few minutes ago...

EDEL. What? Why?

LIAM. When Mairead and the lads... went. You were so sad, I just thought...

EDEL. I'm glad you didn't.

LIAM. Well, good. Did you notice?

EDEL. I'm not minding you half the time.

LIAM. That's it... I think. The worst stuff... that I can remember anyway.

EDEL. It's done. You don't need to push me away. I'm not going anywhere now, am I?

LIAM. I haven't been good Edel...

EDEL. Neither have I ... *(Pause.)* Okay... let's... all we have is this, now. And I know you never wanted to live out here and I know you resented Patrick for what happened –

LIAM. – no, I just... he was a young lad. Off the rails. I resent myself for cutting him off like I did. For all those years. Making Christmases awkward on you and Mairead and... I'm sorry.

EDEL. You got to say goodbye and tell him you love him. You have that. I don't.

LIAM. Yeah...

(Another explosion booms closer.)

What was it came between us, do you think?

EDEL. Life. It was probably just life.

LIAM. And did we try our best, do you think?

EDEL. It doesn't matter now. But yeah. Yeah, we gave it a good shot.

(**LIAM** *picks up the pile of papers he's typed out. He hands them to* **EDEL**.)

LIAM. Anyway, this is for you. I don't know if you'll get to read it.

EDEL. Happy anniversary.

LIAM. We've had worse ones.

EDEL. We have...

(**LIAM** *smiles. They both do.* **EDEL** *takes the manuscript. Then after a moment, there's another explosion in the distance.* **LIAM** *walks to the window and looks out at what's coming.* **EDEL** *looks at the manuscript a few moments, then she puts it down.*)

LIAM. It looks... it's actually beautiful.

EDEL. Liam?

LIAM. Yes?

EDEL. What was the last thing you wrote?

LIAM. 'The End.'

EDEL. No, before that.

LIAM. "I loved her then. I'll love her until the end of the world."

(*Pause. Then:*)

EDEL. Liam?

LIAM. Yes?

EDEL. Will you hold my hand?

(*Pause. Then he walks to her. He takes her hand and looks at it.*)

LIAM. Is that a scar?

EDEL. Yes.

LIAM. When did you get it?

EDEL. Remember I cut my hand chopping wood? When Frank knocked into me?

LIAM. When was that?

EDEL. Three years ago.

LIAM. I never noticed it before now.

EDEL. No?

LIAM. No.

> *(They pause. The noise of destruction gets louder. Music still comes through the noise.*)*

EDEL. Will you put your arm around me?

LIAM. I will.

> *(He does. He draws her close to him. They settle into each other. Hands in hands.)*

EDEL. This is grand.

LIAM. It is. Lovely and grand.

EDEL. Will you maybe sway with me a little?

LIAM. I will.

EDEL. Thanks.

> *(They sway to the music*. The building starts to shake. A strong wind breaks into the room, sending the back door flying open. Everything begins to rattle. The pile of papers that make up **LIAM**'s memoirs are blown all*

---

* A licence to produce DENOUEMENT does not include a performance licence for any third-party or copyrighted music. Licensees should create an original composition or use music in the public domain. For further information, please see Music Use Note on page iii

over the place. Their gaze still remains fixed ahead as they sway and move together, like a tiny slow dance. There is a crash outside. **EDEL** *looks up at the ceiling. She smiles.* **LIAM** *draws her tight to him. They put their heads together, still slowly swaying to the music. Then plaster begins to rain down from the ceiling. The building shakes some more, and them with it.)*

(Then:)

(It all falls. Blackout. Music stops dead. The explosions ring out through the countryside. There's the faint sound of screams. But not many or for long. Then it all ends. Everything.)

The End

ABOUT THE AUTHOR

John is originally from Kilkenny, Ireland. Plays include *Taboo* (White Label); *War Of Attrition, Scratcher, Smitten, Heart Shaped Vinyl* (Devious Theatre) as well as *The Roaring Banshees* and *The Hellfire Squad*, co-written with Peter McGann. He also wrote the stage adaptation of Thomas Kilroy's novel *The Big Chapel* (Asylum/Abbey Theatre/Kilkenny Arts Festival). Other work includes: *Home Theatre Ireland* (Dublin Theatre Festival) and the community theatre project *Bridge Street Will Be* (Equinox/Asylum)

TV work includes the series *Dead Still* for which he won an Edgar Award. Short films include *Seanie & Flo* (Deadpan Pictures); *Kathleen* (Paradox Pictures); *Two Cats* and *Daffney Molloy and Other Catastrophes* (Mycrofilms). Writing for radio includes the serial *Vultures* and the award-winning plays *100 Everyday Menaces* and an adaptation of *The War Of The Worlds*.

Lightning Source UK Ltd.
Milton Keynes UK
UKHW021823130922
408810UK00009B/1374